POULTRY KEEPING

THIS book is intended as a handy guide for all who keep or intend to keep poultry. It is full of valuable information and answers the essential questions raised by poultry keepers, both large and small.

The author is a man of wide experience, having been associated with commercial, pedigree and research poultry flocks. His advice is sound and practical.

A FOYLES HANDBOOK

POULTRY KEEPING

BY

CHARLES G. STACEY, C.P.F. (P.A.G.B.)

Member of the World's Poultry Science Association
Member of the Poultry Association of Great Britain
Member of the Autosexing Breeds Association

With a chapter on Hygiene and Sanitation

by

Dr. R. F. GORDON, M.R.C.V.S

Director, Animal Health Trust Poultry
Research Station

W. & G. FOYLE LTD.
119-125 CHARING CROSS ROAD, LONDON, W.C.2.

First published 1949

Reprinted May 1951

Reprinted September 1952

Revised edition January 1955

Reprinted January 1959

Reprinted October 1963

© W. & G. FOYLE LTD. 1959

Printed in Great Britain
by Ebenezer Baylis and Son, Ltd
The Trinity Press, Worcester, and London

CONTENTS

Photographs by Francis V. Stacey
and reproduced with her permission

PREFACE

DURING the last thirty years a great deal has been discovered about the domestic fowl. Much of this knowledge was acquired the hard way by those men and women who started poultry farms soon after the 1914-18 war. The transition of poultry keeping from the realm of the show bench to that of the commercial egg farm broke many hearts and even more pockets. So many of the enthusiasts who took up the struggle of making the hen a paying proposition had no experience and only the barest outline of theoretical knowledge to guide them. That there were failures in such circumstances was inevitable. Pioneering is always hard and only a number make the grade.

Some of these early pioneers—through sound common sense and a great deal of hardship—established specialist poultry farms which have endured even till to-day. In fact, some of our best-known breeders entered the industry during the early pioneering days. But their task was not easy. Expert help was not available and scientists had not then directed their minds to the numerous problems arising when large numbers of poultry are gathered together in a comparatively restricted area.

The position has altered greatly since then. Keen practical men have given their advice in books and in the poultry press. Some of the best brains in the scientific world have studied disease, equipment and breeding methods, and there is a regular flow of highly technical information from the various research institutions.

In the preparation of this work I have endeavoured to present the facts clearly and in such a way that the beginner will be able to understand what to do, and what is just as important, why he is doing it.

A good sound knowledge of the basic requirements of the fowl coupled with attention to details will enable the poultry-man to face the unexpected and to tackle the problems which arise during the day-to-day management of the flock. Knowing why is the key to most of the snags in any walk of life. It is easy to follow a list of instructions which details how much to feed, when to feed, and what to feed, but it is far better to know the basis of poultry nutrition. If you once learn this fundamental lesson you can then feed your stock irrespective of the varying feeding stuffs that may come your way. The sudden withdrawal of a particular food from the market—a thing we are likely to experience for some years yet—or the appearance of a new bye-product of some industrial process does not leave you in doubt, nor are you easy prey for the go-ahead salesman who wants to dispose of some so-called super poultry food. You can assess the value of such commodities in terms of their actual feeding value.

The same thing applies to housing and equipment. If you know what the fowl needs you can judge as well as the next man whether a new type of house or a new gadget will do its job satisfactorily.

For a number of years now I have been answering the queries sent into one of the National poultry papers. I have also seen a large number of poultry plants—both domestic and commercial. My experience has taught me that there is no one correct way of managing a poultry flock. There are certain essential requirements to success, but nearly every successful poultryman has his own pet system and methods. There is often considerable controversy in the poultry press over some aspects of management or about the virtues of a new item of equipment. The truth generally is that both points of view are right. It does depend so much on the circumstances ruling on each particular farm.

In rearing, for instance, one school of thought is enthusiastic over the use of wire floors in the brooders. A large number of poultrymen, however, decry this method as unnatural and most undesirable. During the last three or four years I have used both methods and each gave satisfactory results. There are many other similar examples which go to prove that, providing you understand why you are doing a certain thing and that you really like the methods you are using, you should get satisfactory results.

THE DORMY HOUSE,
HOUGHTON GRANGE,
HUNTINGDON.

C. G. STACEY,
June, 1949.

CHAPTER I
THE STOCK

The Best Breeds

1. It is general in most books on poultry keeping to give a comprehensive list of breeds and to go into detail regarding the merits and otherwise of each variety. Even to-day with the knowledge available there is still a great deal of difference of opinion regarding the best breed for any particular purpose. It is not therefore proposed in this short volume to deal exhaustively with all the numerous breeds in existence. A general review of the commoner varieties will be of more value to the beginner as most of the popular commercial breeds are suitable for either egg production or table bird work providing you pick from a group suitable for the job you have in mind. There is, in fact, no one breed that can be classed as the best.

The Three Groups

2. From the practical man's point of view we can place all the breeds of poultry into three main groups as follows:

    (a)   Ornamental Breeds

    (b)   Egg producing Breeds

    (c)   Dual Purpose Breeds

Ornamental Breeds

3. The first group—the birds with beautiful or extraordinary feathers—have little value except for the poultry fancier. Such stock is bred entirely for its appearance, and generally speaking shows little financial return to the breeder. To the man who likes living things and is interested in breeding for its own sake these rather exotic breeds make an interesting hobby. But the man who wants eggs either to sell or for his own table is advised to leave them severely alone. By this I do not mean that the fancier has no place in the world of poultry. Indeed, in the past the "Fancy" as it is termed did much to produce our modern varieties and to keep alive a fine spirit of competition which resulted in better and more virile stock.

4. The show bench has been strongly criticised in recent years because extreme fashions have been responsible for the decline in the economic qualities of some really good breeds, but we should not forget the part played by some specialist breeders in ensuring the continuity of vigour and health in our birds. A good example of this is one of the oldest breeds in this country, namely the Old English Game. Fitness was the first requirement of the birds in the cockpit and although cock fighting has been illegal for many years now the breeders of this variety have kept intact this quality of health and stamina in their birds. Many commercial poultry farmers to-day look with envy on these qualities which are still maintained in this most interesting of British breeds.

5. It would be impossible to detail the many breeds and varieties of ornamental poultry as these are essentially for the hobbyist rather than the commercial or domestic poultryman. Anyone who would like to know more about the art of breeding for exhibition could not do better than visit the National Poultry Show held annually in London, or failing that go to one of the local poultry shows held in most neighbourhoods during the autumn and winter. There are usually anything between ten and thirty such breeds on show, and you will certainly get enthusiastic advice from the exhibitors.

Egg Producing Breeds

6. The second group—the egg producers—is not so clearly defined now as in the past. Officially the specialised egg laying varieties are the light breeds that seldom go broody and which do not make good carcasses for the table. It is not true, however, to say that these varieties are superior to all others as producers of eggs. Some of the dual purpose breeds have records equal to or greater than the Leghorns and Minorcas for example. Certainly in America and in some continental countries the White Leghorn is highly favoured in commercial egg production flocks. In the case of the U.S.A. though we must take into consideration the fact that the consumers prefer a white shelled egg and the Leghorn does produce excellent size eggs without pigment. In this country the preference is for eggs with a richly tinted shell, and in normal times this factor should be considered by the commercial egg farmer. One advantage possessed by the light breeds is that they

require slightly less food than the dual purpose fowls. They have smaller bodies and consequently need less material for maintenance than the heavier breeds. In practice this does not always work out but over large numbers there should be some saving in the annual food bill if the stock is properly managed and rationed correctly.

7. One disadvantage sometimes advanced against this group of birds is that they still retain considerable flying abilities and at least six foot wire netting is needed to keep them in the pens. Some Leghorns may even need netting eight feet high to prevent the various groups from mixing. They are also rather nervous and need to be managed quietly, if the intensive system is adopted.

8. The most important breeds in the egg producing group are detailed below. There are, of course, many others but they are of little value to the average commercial or domestic poultry keeper.

White Leghorn	Minorca
Black Leghorn	Ancona
Brown Leghorn	Legbar

9. All the above are non-sitters. This means that they do not usually exhibit the tendency to broodiness. Some strains, in fact, are almost entirely free from the desire to sit, but usually a few birds in the flock will go broody during the late spring and early summer. These breeds lay white shelled eggs and have a very active nature. One of the most popular varieties of this group at present is the White Leghorn, and deservedly so. It has proved itself a good layer of large eggs. Unfortunately it has, during the past decade, been subjected to a good deal of unwise breeding for high egg production with the result that some strains have lost body size and stamina rather badly. There are, however, some excellent strains available and for the man who studies his feeding costs and buys the right type of bird they should prove extremely reliable.

10. The Black Leghorn is also a very good layer and has not been subjected to such extremes in breeding. Good hardy stock is procurable and there is a growing interest in this variety. It has the disadvantage that it is exceptionally active and highly strung and unless carefully managed is easily frightened. It has good flying abilities and eight feet netting is recommended to keep the birds under control.

11. The Brown Leghorn is not so popular as the other two varieties although there is really good stock to be had. It is generally regarded as not quite such a prolific layer but this is really a question of strain. There are a number of flocks in existence with really good egg production figures. With all breeds and varieties the importance of securing a good strain cannot be too highly emphasized. Birds produced by a skilled breeder are naturally very much better than those turned out irrespective of quality or health.

12. The Minorca has of recent years declined considerably in popularity due to the fact that breeding for exhibition points has resulted in reduced egg yield. It is, however, a handsome bird and in the right hands could no doubt be re-created as a first-class layer.

13. The Ancona is very similar to the Black Leghorn in appearance. It is a hardy bird and a good layer, and should enjoy more popularity than it does at present.

14. The Legbar is one of the new auto-sexing breeds evolved at Cambridge and has the advantage that the chicks can be sexed on their down colour at day-old. The value of this factor is considerable. The small poultryman who has only a limited amount of food at his disposal cannot afford to rear all the cockerels produced until their sex can be determined. He also cannot usually avail himself of the services of a professional chick sexer. The Legbar, however, enables him to remove the cockerels as soon as they are hatched. The saving in the cost of rearing the pullets is therefore large. So far this new breed has not equalled the more popular and well established varieties on the score of egg production, and it would appear that the producers of this breed still have quite a lot to do before it takes its place as a top line egg producer. A number of experienced breeders have started work on the problem and it is reasonable to assume that the Legbar will in the future have a definite place in the British poultry industry.

Dual Purpose Birds

15. Group three—the dual purpose birds—is perhaps the most valuable for both the commercial and the domestic

poultry keeper. In the main they are prolific egg producers and give cockerels with plenty of flesh at a comparatively early age. For many years the Rhode Island Red has won the main honours at the National Laying Test which proves the value of at least one member of the group as an egg producer. The Light Sussex, too, is also a good layer and one of the best table birds.

16.   The more popular breeds in this group comprise the following:

Rhode Island Red	White Wyandotte
Light Sussex	Orpington
Buff Plymouth Rock	New Hampshire Red
Barred Plymouth Rock	North Holland Blue

17.   The Rhode Island Red is undoubtedly the most popular breed of poultry in this country to-day. Wherever chickens are kept, there you will find the Rhode. It is a hardy, big bodied bird with an egg production record unbeaten by any other breed. The cockerels make reasonable table birds, but the flesh is yellow and the breast bone rather high. With such large numbers of breeding flocks there is, of course, considerable variation in quality and the mere fact that Rhode Island Red birds are purchased does not necessarily ensure that you will get good laying stock. It pays to buy from a breeder of repute if you want really fecund pullets.

18.   There is, in some quarters, a certain amount of criticism of this breed because of the colour variation in some strains. The true red tint is difficult to maintain, but for the person interested in egg production the question of pure show bench colour can be ignored. There is, naturally, added pleasure in possessing a good evenly-coloured flock of Rhodes, but the economic qualities of fecundity, health and stamina should never be sacrificed for what is, after all, merely an arbitrary fashion standard.

19.   The New Hampshire Red is closely allied to the Rhode Island Red having been made from the latter breed in America. It is a good layer and possesses a hardy constitution. Although of recent introduction into England it has attracted a good deal of interest and may have quite a useful part to play in the future as a dual purpose breed.

20. The Light Sussex is essentially a British breed and was developed originally in the South Eastern part of the country as a table bird, for which purpose it ranks among the very best. During the last few years it has been bred intensively for egg production as well. In the process a certain amount of body size has been lost in many strains but even so it is a remarkably good dual purpose fowl. Egg production, in general, is not quite so good as the Rhode Island Red, but still high enough to warrant its selection by many poultrymen as their breed. There has been a tendency recently to give more attention to body size and some strains are now excellent for both good laying and table qualities.

21. Both the Buff Plymouth Rock and the Barred Plymouth Rock are excellent dual purpose breeds. The Buff is the more popular in this country and is gaining popularity every year. Egg production is good and the cockerels are excellent except for the prejudice that exists against yellow skin. The Barred variety also has put up some exceptionally good laying records and in Canada it is regarded very highly indeed. There is, however, in some strains a definite leaning towards small egg size but this is a fault which could be corrected with a suitable breeding programme.

22. The North Holland Blue is similar in appearance to the Barred Rock except that the barring is less regular and that some strains show a tendency to feathered legs. It is a good table bird, and is also a useful layer.

23. The story of the White Wyandotte is a sad one. Originally it was one of the most popular breeds, and flocks of these attractive birds were to be seen all over the countryside. Unfortunately, breeding for high egg production brought in its train reduced stamina, poor fertility and a general decline in usefulness. At its best it is an excellent layer and first grade table bird, but really good stock is difficult to acquire. It is not now generally regarded as a good investment, but if a good strain can be bought it is still a worthwhile proposition.

Choosing a Breed

24. The above-mentioned breeds and varieties are the most popular among poultry keepers to-day. There are also many others, but the beginner, in choosing his breed, would be well advised to keep to those that have proved their worth with

commercial poultry farmers. A breed is popular because it can pay its way. Before making a choice make an endeavour to see as many of the breeds as possible. The poultry shows will help to a certain extent, but it is far better to observe the birds under their actual working conditions. Finally, select a breed you like because in all aspects of poultry keeping you will find that you are more likely to make a success if you choose the system and the stock for which you have a natural preference.

Buying Stock

25. When a decision has been made regarding the breed there then arises the very important question of where to buy the stock. Very often the success or otherwise of the venture is decided by the quality of the birds bought. Good birds are a sound investment even though the initial outlay is comparatively high. Stock of low vitality and poor productive ability is dear even if you get the birds for nothing! A third-rate specimen laying say eighty to one hundred eggs during her first season eats very nearly as much as the vigorous healthy pullet that may easily produce 180–200 eggs during the same period.
26. It therefore pays to buy the best stock you can afford. I most strongly suggest that you DO NOY BUY PULLETS OR FOR THAT MATTER ANY CLASS OF POULTRY FROM A MARKET. Every commercial poultry farmer has a few duds each year and it is the normal practice to cull such birds and send them to a dealer or local market for what they will fetch. No breeder of repute would ever offer such stock for sale in the normal way. Anything he sells under his own name is usually up to a reasonable standard of quality.
27. There is no such implied guarantee with birds bought from an auction market. Many of the recent fowl pest outbreaks were traced to the sale of infected birds at markets and by dealers. Therefore, buy your birds—whether they be day-old chicks or point-of-lay pullets, from a man whose livelihood depends on satisfied customers. The Ministry of Agriculture has approved certain farms in each county under its Accredited Poultry Breeding Scheme as being units where a certain standard of hygiene and management is maintained. From these farms you can expect to get a fair deal. Not all the birds they sell are super layers neither is there any guarantee that the stock will not contract disease and die, but as far as possible the

Accredited Poultry Breeders do turn out a really good class of bird.

28. The farms under this scheme are visited regularly by Government inspectors, and unless the breeding stock and the management is up to a definite standard the farm is removed from the approved lists. You can get the address of the accredited breeders in your district from the local Agricultural Executive Committee or from the area organiser of the Domestic Poultry Keepers' Council. The addresses of the area organisers are given at the end of this chapter. If you have any difficulty in getting your stock you can obtain helpful advice from these officials at no cost to yourself. They will be able to put you on the right track.

29. Information on judging the quality of birds is given in Chapter Six and before buying your stock it is advisable to note in your own mind the general appearance of healthy vigorous fowls. Even the novice should be able to recognise the signs of health and stamina. Poor quality stock usually betrays its lack of quality in its general behaviour and dejected appearance.

*   *   *

DOMESTIC POULTRY KEEPERS' COUNCIL
Area Organisers

Northern

Northumberland, Durham, Yorkshire (North Riding), Cumberland, Westmorland, North Lancashire (North of line Carnforth, Ingleton to Yorkshire border).

139 Newgate Street, Bishop Auckland.

North Midland

Lancashire (other than Northern part indicated above), Yorkshire, East Riding, West Riding, Cheshire, Derbyshire, Nottinghamshire, Lindsey Division of Lincolnshire.

(2nd Floor) 52 Corporation Street, Manchester, 4.

Midland

Staffordshire, Shropshire, Herefordshire, Worcestershire, Warwickshire, Leicestershire, Rutlandshire, Northamptonshire, Kesteven Division of Lincolnshire.

Cavendish House, Waterloo Street, Birmingham, 2.

Wales

All counties and Monmouth.

1 St. Andrew's Place, Cardiff.

Eastern

Huntingdom, Cambridgeshire, Norfolk, Suffolk, Isle of Ely, Essex, Herts, Soke of Peterborough and Holland Division of Lincolnshire.

Neale House, Neale Street, Ipswich.

South Western

Wiltshire, Somerset, Dorset, Devon, Cornwall, Gloucestershire.

3 Haines Hill Terrace, Taunton.

Southern

Hants, Isle of Wight, Berks, Oxon, Bucks, Bedford.

Foyers, Woodlands, Nr. Southampton, Hampshire.

London and South Eastern

Middlesex, London, Kent, Surrey, Sussex, Metropolitan districts of Hertfordshire and Essex.

14-16 Wood's Mews, Park Lane, London, W.1.

CHAPTER II

HOUSING

Systems

30. To give a proper appreciation of the usefulness of the numerous types of houses on the market it is necessary first of all to outline briefly the various systems under which poultry flocks are maintained. The same principle applies here as in the case of Stock—it is better to buy good quality houses of the right type for the system adopted than to economise at the expense of efficiency. Do not be guided entirely by price and ignore the question of suitability. A house that may work well with one system of management may fail disastrously with another.

Free Range

31. There are at present five widely different methods of managing poultry, all of which have their value in the right circumstances. The first is that of allowing the birds practically unlimited free range. The flock is allowed to graze over comparatively large fields and no attempt is made to restrict its movements apart from confining it to the limits of the particular field concerned. Such methods obviously apply only where plenty of space is available and the stock can do little or no damage to the land over which it runs. Generally the free range system is limited to farms with large areas of grassland and corn stubble, or to some fruit growers who utilize the spare land round the trees. It is a good system in so far that the housing costs are low and the birds do manage to pick up quite a proportion of their food providing the land is not overstocked. Its disadvantages are that any form of control is difficult and egg production may be lower due to the exposed conditions in bad weather plus the fact that a number of birds will persist in "laying away" or depositing their eggs in some secret nest.

Colony Houses

32. Two types of houses are popular for this system. One

is the rather out-of-date colony house which is equipped with a littered floor, perches and nest boxes. It cannot be said that the average colony house is a great success. Usually there are too many birds accommodated for the size of the house—the general principle being that the unit will hold as many birds as can be "put up" for the night. All houses with solid floors have a capacity limited by the ventilating system, and unless this is extremely efficient there is bound to be overcrowding when the stock is allowed less than $2\frac{1}{2}/3$ square feet per bird.

Slatted Floor House

33. A more recent development for the housing of birds on free range is the slatted floor house. This is usually mounted on wheels or skids for easy moving and has as its distinguishing feature a floor of wooden slats placed about $1\frac{1}{2}$ in. apart. The idea is that a unit of any given size can accommodate

FIG. 1

A typical free range slatted floor house. (Manufactured by Tom M. Scotney Ltd.)

many more birds if there is a free flow of air through the building. There is usually an open ridge to the house (protected by a baffle to prevent the entry of rain, etc.) which serves as the outlet for the stale air. The nest boxes are usually arranged down either side of the house and are raised off the slats so as to allow full use to be made of the floor area for sleeping purposes. No perches are provided as the birds sleep on the slats. There is likewise no floor litter, and the birds' droppings fall through the gaps between the slats on to a droppings' board which can be cleaned periodically. With this type of housing it is usual to allow about $\frac{3}{4}$/1 square foot of free floor space per bird. A 6 ft. x 7 ft. unit will therefore accommodate approximately fifty pullets in comfort. Equipment manufacturers are notorious for their optimistic statements regarding the capacity of their houses and you will often see houses of this size recommended for up to seventy-five adults.

34. True, a 6 ft. x 7 ft. slatted floor house will sleep this number of birds, but there is a very definite danger of overcrowding with all its attendant troubles. A good practical test of whether a house is overcrowded is to visit it at night after the birds have been settled in for three or four hours. If the atmosphere inside is thick and unpleasant then there is overcrowding and the man who wants the best results will take immediate steps to reduce the number of birds.

35. Most of the models on the market are good as the basic principle is sound. There are, however, in some cases too many "gadgets." Built-in mash hoppers and water troughs appear at first sight to be a good idea, but in actual practice these are seldom used, as the birds' feeding utensils are normally placed in the run. This latter arrangement is better as it permits ample trough space. If the built-in fittings only are used there will be insufficient feeding space, with the result that the weaker and less aggressive members of the flock will be underfed. This in turn leads to reduced egg yields, poorer health and possibly to the poultry farmer's greatest dread—disease.

36. It is much better to save the cost of these built-in fittings and to buy well designed separate feeding and watering equipment which can be placed near the house in accordance with any special method of feeding.

Fold Units

37. Another type of housing admirably suitable for the man with plenty of land is the fold unit holding approximately twenty-five birds. This system of folding as it is called is a comparatively recent innovation and is gaining more adherents every year. It has the advantage over the free range meteods that the stock is under complete control and that better use can

FIG. 2

A modern wood and wire netting fold unit of light weight construction equipped with built-in food and water troughs, broody breaking coop and separate nest box compartment.
(Manufactured by Papworth Industries).

be made of the land. The normal practice is to move the folds, their own length or width each morning. This has two big advantages over the normal free range system. It ensures that the whole area of ground is covered equally by the birds and that there are no patches of mud near the houses. Secondly, it ensures that the stock is always on clean soil with the result that the risk of parasitic infection is greatly reduced. Fold units will improve the pasture over which they are moved and many farmers who use this system go so far as to say that even if their poultry flocks were being run at a loss they would still retain them because of the improvement they make to the land.

38. A small number of folds can often be used to good effect in a well-spaced orchard. The units can be moved forward between the trees and as the birds are under complete control there is no danger of injury to low hanging fruit.

39.   This system has much to recommend it. The labour bill
is quite low as there is no cleaning out to be done apart from
occasionally scraping the slatted floor sleeping compartment,
and as the birds are usually fed on dry mash or pellets the
time spent on feeding is reduced to a minimum. The system
does, however, need plenty of land. A 20 ft. x 6 ft. fold moving
forward six days a week requires a run of about one mile in a
year or approximately 4/5ths of an acre. This assumes that the
fold is not returned over ground it has already used that season.
40.   Essentially the fold unit consists of a slatted floor sleeping
compartment equipped with nest boxes plus a built-on wire
run. A good sized unit for twenty-five birds measures twenty
feet long by five feet wide. The sleeping compartment extends
about four feet from one end and the run is approximately
sixteen feet long by five feet wide. There are now a large
number of fold units being manufactured commercially, and
some difficulty may be experienced in making a choice. One
of the main factors to be borne in mind is the question of
weight. These houses have to be moved DAILY and unless
the attendant is as strong as the proverbial ox the exertion
required can be very great unless a light-weight model is
chosen. There are some very good models in resin bonded
plywood and aluminium, but prices are rather high. A
satisfactory fold can be constructed cheaply with the minimum
of timber from wooden battening, roofing felt and wire
netting.

Semi-intensive System

41.   The most popular method of keeping poultry at present
is undoubtedly the semi-intensive system which consists of a
fixed house providing laying and sleeping quarters and a wire
netting run or runs. Most commercial poultry farms are laid
out on these lines. The system is convenient to work as a
comparatively large number of birds can be accommodated
on a small area of land. It has, however, one serious difficulty
and that is the problem of keeping the land from becoming
fowlsick with consequent loss from disease. Good results are
often obtained for the first few years, but as the ground
becomes increasingly contaminated with poultry droppings
there is frequently a reduction in egg yield and an increase
in the number of deaths.

42. This is really the hardest system of all to operate successfully and calls for a great deal of skill and knowledge on the part of the poultryman. It is unfortunate that most domestic and small-scale poultry keepers adopt this method. Until quite recently they had very little choice, but with the advent of the laying battery and the fully intensive poultry house I do advise them to leave the semi-intensive methods alone. More often than not their small grass pens degenerate rapidly into patches of mud which make the management of the flock unpleasant and difficult in bad weather, and at the same time provide ideal breeding conditions for many of the common diseases and parasites of poultry.

43. The type of house recommended for use with the semi-intensive system consists of a solid floor house equipped with next boxes and perches. There is usually a layer of litter some 3/4 in. deep on the floor. To get the best results it is desirable to allow ample floor space and four to five sq. ft. per bird is not too much. Many poultrymen give the stock much less room than this, but as I have said the system is extremely difficult to operate successfully for long periods, and unless you are an experienced poultry keeper it is better to play for safety and be generous with the floor space. Another important factor is head room for the operator. Litter must be changed frequently and during the winter months the birds may have to be fed and watered inside. Unless the house is at least 5½/6 ft. high the attendant will find his work very fatiguing. Nowadays it is generally considered that the semi-intensive house should be designed on the same lines and allow the same amount of space as the fully intensive unit.

Intensive System

44. The completely intensive system of poultry keeping has recently gained considerable popularity. For the man with a limited amount of land there is much to be said in favour of this method. Large numbers of birds can be maintained on a comparatively small plot of ground and, providing the system is properly understood and well managed, the results should be comparable with the more usual methods. Essentially, intensivism means confining the stock entirely to a modified laying house. As the birds have no contact with the land they do not suffer from the bad effects of "fowlsick"

or disease-contaminated ground, and up to 2,000 birds can be maintained to the acre. It is necessary, however, to remember that as there is no possibility of the birds adding to their diet by grazing they must be provided with a well-balanced ration complete with the essential vitamins and minerals. Secondly the capital cost of housing is high unless suitable buildings are available which can be converted cheaply. There is also a tendency for intensively kept birds to develop such vices as cannibalism and egg eating.

45. Success depends on two fundamental things—(a) the right type of house and (b) a good diet. The house must provide ample floor space and fresh air and should also allow direct sunlight to enter during the day. A minimum area per bird of 4½/5 sq. ft. is desirable. With large numbers— say 500 birds to a house—a little less has proved satisfactory, but with small pens of 6/12 this figure should be increased to at least six sq. ft. per bird.

46. One side of the house should be fitted with removable shutters which should be opened during the day irrespective of the temperature outside. The only time they should be closed is to prevent driving wind or rain blowing in on the litter. In summer they can be left open day and night. For good results and easy management an intensive laying house should be not less than 6 ft. high at the eaves and 8½ ft. at the ridge and should be at least 12 ft. wide. Narrow houses tend to make the stock nervous when the attendant is servicing the food and water troughs, etc. If possible a width of 15 ft. should be allowed. Baffled air intakes at floor level and a centre ridge gap to allow the extraction of the stale air should be fitted to provide efficient ventilation, when the outer shutters are closed.

Converting Existing Buildings

47. These days the erection of special houses is an expensive business but it is often possible to convert an existing building. A small barn or open fronted cart shed can be reconstructed to make a very good intensive house at small cost. The front of the building can be boarded up to a height of 2 ft. from the ground and the remainder filled in with 2/2½ in. wire netting. Shutters made from roofing felt or glass substitute nailed to light frames and held in place by large turnbuttons can be

added although if the building is well sheltered these are not essential. The interior can be divided into pens by means of wire netting divisions equipped with frame doors to permit easy movement by the poultryman from one section to another. The usual perches, nest boxes, feeding troughs, etc., must be installed but these items are more or less standard fittings and present no special difficulties.

48.   In America the intensive system has been developed to a remarkable degree and some of the larger plants are four and five storied buildings resembling well-lighted factories. Providing the essential points of ample floor space, plenty of direct light and good ventilation are kept in mind most buildings can be utilised when adapted.

The Laying Battery

49.   Perhaps the best system for the poultry keeper with little or no land at his disposal is the most intensive of all methods of managing poultry—the laying battery. This system has been developed over the last 15/18 years but it is only of recent years that it has gained its present popularity.

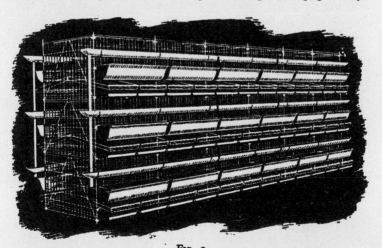

Fig. 3
A seventy-two bird laying battery unit of all wire construction
(Manufactured by Cope & Cope Ltd.).

It enables poultry to be kept in the smallest of "back-yards" without creating the poultry slums so typical of the restricted earth plots seen in so many town gardens. For years experienced poultrymen have known that, other factors being equal, the smaller the number of birds housed together the greater the egg production, and that the obvious ideal unit was the single bird. Naturally it is impossible to provide individual houses for each layer both on the grounds of the initial cost of equipment and the enormous labour bill which would arise in attending to the flock. The laying battery does, in effect, provide single bird housing and at the same time reduces labour charges. Each bird is housed in a separate wooden or metal cage of special construction and these cages are grouped together in tiers and rows according to the number of birds required.

Advantages of Laying Batteries

50. Small six bird units are popular with domestic poultry keepers and the commercial plants run anything from 250 to 5,000 birds on this system with equal success. The advantages of the battery system are legion. Briefly they can be summed up as follows:—

(a) There is complete control over the stock and feather plucking, cannibalism and egg eating are eliminated

(b) There is an automatic check on the egg production of each layer and the unprofitable birds can be sent to table without waste of food

(c) As each bird gets its fair share of food and water and there is no bullying egg production is generally higher than from any other system

(d) The risk of disease is greatly reduced as the birds are on a wire floor and cannot come into contact with the contaminated droppings of other birds

(e) There is no need for litter and the eggs are very much cleaner

(f) It is possible to look after comparatively large numbers of birds in spare time, as the stock can be left all day if necessary once they have been provided with food and water

(g) There is no need for separate pens for pullets and hens as each bird is a unit on its own

(h) Finally, birds housed in the cages remain tender and after their useful laying life is over they still make good birds for the table

51. The essentials of success with this system are:—

(a) A properly designed laying cage

(b) Efficient ventilation of the building used for the

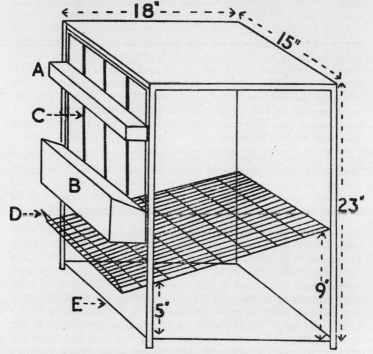

FIG. 4 DETAILS OF LAYING CAGE CONSTRUCTION:

(A) Water container, (B) Food trough, (C) Removable front with wires placed 2¼ in. apart, (D) Wire floor projecting six inches from front of cage, (E) Droppings tray removable for easy cleaning. The wire fronts and floors can be bought ready made from equipment manufacturers. Alternatively 1 inch mesh 16 guage wire netting can be used for the floor if tacked to a 1 in. x 1½ in. wooden framing.

battery if it is an indoor model
and
(c)   A well balanced diet

52.   There is no definite standard size for the laying cage but experience has shown that it should be in the region of 15 in. wide by 18 in. deep. The wire floor should slope towards the front and should be equipped with a stop to prevent the eggs rolling on to the floor. The illustration in Fig. 4 indicates the general principle on which laying cages are usually built. Anyone handy with tools can easily construct a bank of cases using wood and wire netting, but there are many excellent models on the market to choose from. Most manufacturers now produce their laying battery cages on the unit principle and the outfit can be added to as required. The larger models frequently incorporate automatic watering and cleaning devices which reduce labour still further. There are even several on the market which provide automatic feeding equipment, but these are designed more for the large scale commercial egg farmer.

53.   The special wire floors and cage fronts can be purchased separately so the man who wants to make up his own outfit can do so without much difficulty providing he can do the necessary wood work. Mash troughs and drinkers can also be bought, but they are comparatively easy to produce at home.

54.   Laying batteries are usually placed in a well ventilated and lighted building, but they can be operated outdoors providing reasonable protection is given to the birds. With the outdoor models the stock must be sheltered from sun and driving rain. The roof of the top tier should be covered with some waterproof material such as roofing felt and the back and sides of the row must be blocked in. Careful siting of the outfit will help considerably—a location protected from the north is ideal. The stock does not need coddling but merely a chance to get on with the job of egg production without inconvenience from extreme weather conditions. Given reasonably protected surroundings an outdoor laying battery unit will prove very satisfactory and will reduce the initial cost of installation considerably.

55.   When an indoor unit is contemplated it is essential to

have really efficient ventilation. An open fronted shed equipped with shutters for use during inclement weather and at night time in winter, will prove satisfactory if some provision is made to ensure a steady flow of air through the building when the shutters are closed. Air intakes properly baffled to prevent draughts at the ground level and extractor cowls in the roof are the best ideas for good ventilation. The latter can, however, be dispensed with if an horizontal ridge cap is incorporated in the roof. It is also desirable to have roof lights so that the stock is not kept in the semi-darkness when the shutters are closed. Light has an extremely stimulating effect on the laying organs of the fowl and stock kept in well lighted quarters will produce more eggs than birds housed in a dark building.

56. A good test of the ventilation can be made first thing in the morning after the stock has been shut up all night. There should be no offensive odour on entering the building. If there is, then additional air intakes and extractors are required.

57. In connection with the feeding of battery-kept birds the same thing applies as to any other intensively managed stock. The birds are unable to pick up anything from the ground to compensate for any deficiencies and it is therefore essential to provide a ration that will supply all the nutrients required for health and production. Good production and fitness can be expected in the laying cages only if the food is of the right type and quality. It is poor economy to use inferior feeding material.

Choosing a System

58. The foregoing briefly sums up the merits and advantages of the various types of housing commonly used for poultry. There are plenty of systems from which to choose and a choice should be made in accordance with your own particular circumstances. The domestic poultry keeper with only a small garden should obviously think of intensive methods. He can then keep poultry and still retain an attractive garden. His best system is the laying battery as it takes up very little space—an outdoor six-bird unit in two tiers requires an area of only 5 ft. by about 2 ft. 6 in. deep, and the stock is under complete control. The smallholder who has an outbuilding

to spare would also probably choose either an intensive house or the laying battery. A large dairy farmer on the other hand could decide with advantage on the fold unit as he has plenty of grassland at his disposal. He would also reap the benefit of better quality grass as a result of moving the folds across the land.

59. Free range houses—slatted floor or colony type—are suitable for both the general farmer and the fruit grower, but would not be successful on smallholdings where the birds must be kept away from growing crops. As can be seen the choice of system is entirely dependent on the amount of land and the buildings available.

Buying Equipment

60. Once the system has been decided upon the next decision to be made is where to obtain the necessary equipment. If sufficient capital is available the best course is to buy the houses from a poultry equipment manufacturer. There are many firms turning out a variety of houses, cages, etc., and their addresses can be obtained from the pages of the various poultry journals. Get a number of catalogues and compare the design, size and price. One word of advice may perhaps not be out of place here. Practically all appliance manufacturers are optimists and have a tendency towards over estimating the number of birds which their houses will hold. True you usually can get the number of birds "recommended" into the particular house in question but almost invariably you will get better results if you accommodate just a few less than suggested. If you estimate on the basis of a 10 per cent— 15 per cent reduction in the advertised capacity of the house you will not go far wrong.

61. Whether or not you decide to make your own poultry houses and equipment depends mainly on your own skill as a carpenter and also upon your ability to obtain the timber, etc. required. Unless you are skilled at this sort of thing it is really better to buy from a manufacturer. I can well remember a few years ago buying some patent all metal brooders. They were extremely well designed and worked very efficiently but were expensive. It was decided that these could be made for about half the price on the farm and we went ahead full of confidence. We overlooked the fact that sheet metal working

(**A**)   Silver Campine Cockerel

(**B**)   Brown Leghorn Cockerel

(**C**)   Brown Leghorn Pullet

(**D**)   Black Leghorn Pullet

PLATE I

(**A**)   Rhode Island Red Cockerel

(**B**)   Buff Plymouth Rock Cockerel

(**C**)   Silver Laced Wyandotte Pullet

(**D**)   Light Sussex Pullet

PLATE II

is a highly skilled business and it took two of us all our spare time for four weeks to produce a rather sorry looking imitation of the original. We could not in any case make the special lamp used and had to buy this at a very stiff price from the original manufacturers. Taking into account the raw materials and labour we found in the end that instead of saving 50 per cent of the purchase price it had actually cost us more than buying the real thing and we did not have a very efficient brooder for our trouble.

62. But this depends upon your own skill. If you can tackle the job by all means do so, but remember to get hold of a really good design before starting. If timber is limited much can be done to economise by using stout roofing felt backed by wire netting. House sides are just as efficient made this way as they are with wood. The wire netting is first stretched tightly over the framework and the roofing felt is then added. This is cheaper than wood and with care will last ten years providing the felt is tarred and sanded periodically.

63. Surplus aluminium alloy sheeting is also very useful as a substitute for wood but is rather expensive. It can, however, be used to great advantage in the construction of fold units as it is durable and light. The conversion of existing buildings to intensive or semi-intensive houses is much in vogue at present owing to difficulties and expense of erecting new large structures. Such work can often be undertaken in conjunction with a local builder and many previously useless barns, cartsheds, etc., are now being used for poultry flocks.

64. The cardinal points to bear in mind when undertaking such renovations is simplicity of design and good ventilation. Do not incorporate too many gadgets but bear in mind the fundamental requirements of the poultry flock.

65. For those who wish to make their own equipment I give an outline of the various items usually needed, together with comments regarding size, etc., which may be useful.

Feeding Troughs—Dry Mash

66. There is a great variety of styles but the main essential consists of something that is easy to clean, does not encourage waste and is so designed that the birds cannot foul the contents. For dry mash a hopper style container holding about one week's supply is ideal and can be constructed on the lines of

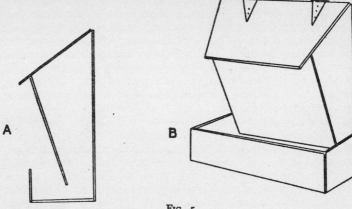

FIG. 5

Simple home-made dry mash hopper. (A) Sectional view showing details of construction. (B) General appearance of hopper.

the illustration in Fig. 5. An allowance of 1 ft. of trough space per ten birds should be adequate.

Feeding Troughs—Wet Mash

67. For wet mash feeding an open "V" shaped trough 6 in. wide is suitable. The length of the trough depends on the number of birds and it is usual to allow at least 2 ft. 6 in. of length for a ten bird unit. The following table gives suggested trough space to allow per 100 birds:—

Age		Space	
Chicks	0 – 3 weeks	6 feet	
,,	3 – 6 ,,	12	,,
,,	6 – 12 ,,	16	,,
Over	12 weeks	20	,,

Metal feeding equipment has much to recommend it as it can be scrubbed and disinfected with ease. It also has the advantage that it is usually lighter than an equivalent wooden construction.

Watering Devices

68. These vary from the open trough type to the ingenious automatic systems now gaining popularity in this country.

The prime consideration when deciding on a container for water is to ensure that:—

(a) It cannot be easily contaminated by droppings
(b) It is easy to clean
(c) It holds sufficient water for the number of birds it serves
(d) It protects the contents from the hot sun
(e) It does not freeze in severe weather

This latter point is of particular importance when installing an automatic system. The following table gives an approximate idea of the amount of water required by fowls of various ages. Naturally this will vary according to the rate of egg production, the type of feeding and the temperature. Heavy egg production requires a corresponding increase in the water requirements of the flock, and this also applies in very hot weather. Birds fed on dry mash or pellets will similarly require more than those fed on a wet mash diet.

Age of Birds	Quantity of water per day*
0—4 weeks	3 pints —$2\frac{1}{4}$ gals.
6—10 ,,	$2\frac{1}{2}$ gals. —$3\frac{1}{2}$,,
12—26 ,,	$3\frac{1}{2}$,, —$4\frac{1}{2}$,,
adults	4 ,, —6 ,,

*Per 100 birds

Water Fount

69. For general cleanliness the fount type of water container (Plate VI, Fig. B) is difficult to beat. Open pans are frequently used but the risk of contamination from the birds' droppings is great unless the unit is provided with a canopy to prevent the stock standing on the sides of the vessel. Intensive houses and laying batteries are frequently fitted with an automatic system based on a constant drip of water from a tap into a trough equipped with an overflow.

70. Whatever type of drinking vessel is used it is a good plan to stand it on a wire netting frame so that any liquid spilled will not be paddled by the birds all over the house or run. With outdoor systems the wire frame can stand over a patch of cinders several inches deep. This will help considerably in keeping the soil dry and will prevent the muddy area commonly seen round the water container.

71. During very hot weather some provision should be made to keep the water cool. A wooden canopy over the trough will

do this. In winter when severe frosts are expected some poultrymen stand the drinking vessels over a "Little Putnan" type heater. Apart from preventing freezing this also helps to keep up egg production as icy cold water is not relished by the stock and any reduction in water consumption will have an adverse effect on laying.

Grit Hoppers

72. This small item of equipment is frequently overlooked in spite of its importance. Unless a plentiful supply of clean flint and also some form of calcium grit is always before the stock there is a risk that:—

    (a)   The birds will not extract all the nourishment possible from the food, and

    (b)   Eggs will be thin or soft shelled

It is therefore good management to provide a weather-proof grit container. A hopper built on the lines of the dry mash container illustrated holding say 28 lbs. of mixed flint grit and crushed oyster shell in the proportion of one part flint to four parts shell will be adequate for a pen of up to 100 layers. It should be checked periodically and refilled long before it is empty.

Perches

73. These are usually provided in all types of accommodation except the slatted floor house, the fold unit and the laying battery where the particular structure makes perching unnecessary or impossible. A good perch should be substantial and made of at least 2 in. x 2 in. material with the top edges rounded off. They are usually placed 3 ft. above the floor level and frequently have a board underneath to hold the droppings. In some houses a droppings pit is installed. This saves labour as cleaning out is done at less frequent intervals.

74. There is a very important point to bear in mind when fitting the perches in a poultry house and that is the fact that red mite (a troublesome poultry parasite) thrives in the crevice provided where the perch fits on to its supports. It is therefore important to have an easily removable fitting. A simple slot in the wood-work is sufficient. Ample perching space is another important point as inadequate roosting accommodation may lead to quarrels among the stock at

roosting time. Allow at least 9 in. per bird for heavy and 8 in. for the light breeds.

Nest Boxes

75. These are essential for laying birds, and to prevent broken and floor eggs one nest box is required for each six pullets housed. Many of those fitted to commercial houses are too small. A good size is 14 in. square by 6 in. deep. The best location for the nests is in the darkest part of the house. Birds prefer to feel isolated when laying, and the subdued light does help to reduce the vice of egg eating to a minimum. It is usual to construct the nests in a line (with a wire netting bottom) to reduce the amount of timber required. A box 7 ft. long by 14 in. wide and 6 in. deep divided into divisions at 14 in. intervals will give six separate nest boxes and provide accommodation for thirty-six—forty layers. The nests are frequently placed about 2 ft. 6 in. from the floor. They should be so constructed that they can be removed for cleaning as dirty nests provide an ideal breeding ground for some of the poultry parasites.

Other Fittings

76. There are many more "gadgets" incorporated in some poultry houses but they are, in the main, unnecessary. A house equipped with the items already mentioned will provide suitable quarters for a laying flock, and the simpler the design the easier it will be to keep the place clean. Good clean surroundings are essential for successful poultry keeping, so concentrate on making all the internal fittings easily removable. Apart from sound construction on common sense lines the only problem likely to arise is that of ventilation. A well ventilated house will be dry and the litter will remain fresh for quite a long period. There are a number of excellent cowls on the market which will ensure adequate ventilation and the manufacturers will advise the correct size for any particular building. While these are extremely efficient it is possible to incorporate sound ventilation in the house itself without this aid. The ridge cap illustrated in Plate IV, Fig. A is satisfactory. Care should be taken to avoid the possibility of down draughts. These arise particularly when the old type ridge capping is used as shown in Plate IV, Fig. B. When

buying a house this point should
be borne in mind as some
manufacturers still incorporate
the old system in their models.

77. The air intake should be
at floor level and can consist of
a number of 1 in. holes bored in
the side of the house. To prevent
draughts these holes should be
baffled and to provide some form
of control a sliding shutter also
bored with 1 in. corresponding
holes should be fitted. By this
method you can adjust the
amount of air passing through
the house to suit the particular
weather conditions prevailing. An
alternative air intake can be made
by cutting out a piece of the
side boarding (6 in. x 4 in.) and
covering the hole with fine perforated zinc. This method is
illustrated in Fig. 6.

78. Apart from the nest boxes
the remainder of the house
should be as light as possible so
choose a design incorporating
good window space. All windows
should be made so that they
can be opened during normal
weather. Do not be afraid of
fresh air in the poultry house.
Far too many people imagine
that they must keep their birds
warm. Nothing is more likely

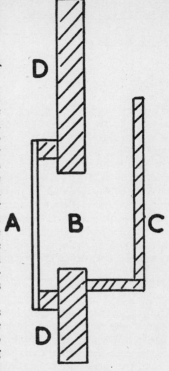

Fig. 6

Details of baffled air inlets to
poultry house: (A) Perforated
zinc. (B) Hole cut in wall of house.
(C) Baffle board to break direct
currents of air. (D) Wall of house.

to lead to disaster. It has been proved that fowls require on a
weight for weight basis, five times as much air as does man.
When, therefore, you go into a poultry house first thing in
the morning and are greeted with a heavy unpleasant atmosphere think how much the birds are suffering. How can they
under such conditions, give the best results?

CHAPTER III

FEEDING

Theory of Nutrition

79. The gulf between theoretical poultry nutrition and practical poultry feeding has always been great, and during the last ten years has, if anything, grown still greater. Before the war many poultry farmers had their own particular ideas upon the composition of an ideal diet and most of them would, for instance, return a consignment of "stale" food immediately to the miller. The severe rationing imposed since the world shortage of feeding stuffs has forced many to change their outlook. Flocks of layers have been fed on materials which would have previously been spurned. Evil smelling—even mouldy—"pudding" (a form of processed kitchen waste), inferior quality cereals and fish fertilizers have been incorporated in the layers' daily mash and very surprisingly have—in many cases—proved quite satisfactory.

80. The reason why such apparently unwholesome material supports life and gives a reasonable rate of egg production is really no mystery. The fowl needs certain nutrients and within reason it does not greatly matter in what form these are supplied, providing the foodstuff concerned is capable of being utilised by the birds. However, practically all the unrationed foods on the market have a tendency towards excessive bulk in relation to the amount of nourishment they contain, and whereas before the war it was generally considered that a laying pullet required about $4\frac{1}{2}$ ozs. of food per day, some rations to-day may need to be supplied at the rate of 10 ozs. or even 12 ozs. if the stock is to produce at a satisfactory level.

81. Now that the rationing of feeding stuffs has been discontinued it is, of course, possible once again to buy ready prepared poultry foods from the millers. These foods, however, are fairly expensive and it is still worth while for the man with a knowledge of nutrition to prepare his own properly balanced diets. Unfortunately, there has been and still is, a great

deal of rubbish for sale to poultry farmers and an under-
standing of the theory of feeding will be of great value in
assessing the true worth of these "special offers."

82. There is nothing very difficult in the fundamental
facts of nutrition and the following remarks are addressed to
the beginner as an introduction to the subject. Most of the
technicalities have been omitted but sufficient detail is given
to enable the prospective poultry keeper to understand why
certain foodstuffs are required and why some of the poor
quality products frequently offered are valueless from the
point of view of egg production.

The Nutrients

83. There are six categories of nutritive material and each
of these plays an essential part in the maintenance of life and
reproduction. A deficiency of one or more of these substances
will lead to lower egg production, poor health and—in
extreme cases—disease and death. The six groups are:—

(i)	Water
(ii)	Proteins
(iii)	Carbohydrates
(iv)	Fats and Oils
(v)	Vitamins
(vi)	Minerals

Water

84. This is perhaps the most important item in the list
as water plays an essential part in every stage of life. Without
it, life in the higher animals is impossible. Fortunately it is
available in unlimited quantities and all who keep poultry
should ensure that it is always provided in ample amounts
and in a clean state. Nothing reduces egg yield so quickly
as insufficient water. Withholding it for only thirty-six hours
will put a flock of layers into a full moult—this latter fact is
sometimes used by poultry farmers who wish to force the
annual moult to begin earlier than usual. A modified form of
water starvation can take place even when the water containers are kept filled—*i.e.*, both very cold and sun heated
water is unpalatable to poultry and in consequence they will
drink less than they need with a corresponding drop in the

number of eggs produced. The moral of providing shelter for the drinking vessels is obvious.

85. Cleanliness of the containers and purity of the supply are important. Water is an ideal carrier of many diseases and unless care is taken to prevent contamination the risk of ailments is high. It is dangerous to allow birds to drink from puddles or ponds as such places are almost certain to be heavily charged with poultry droppings. It is also unwise to make use of a running stream as it is possible for the diseases of another farm further up stream to be carried down to other flocks.

86. Piped water from the main is the best but if this is not available then well or spring water should be used. Rain water collected in covered butts is also suitable if care is taken to prevent contamination. All containers and drinkers should be scrubbed at regular intervals to prevent the formation of slime.

87. All this may sound extreme but an ample supply of good clean water will do much to ensure the success of a poultry venture, and a limited supply of dirty water will— sooner or later—bring disaster. There is really no excuse for water-borne disease as the remedy is in the farmer's own hands and any trouble due to the water supply is rank bad management.

Proteins

88. The protein groups of feeding stuffs are characterised by the fact that they contain the element known as nitrogen, and are extremely important in nutrition as they supply the substances required for the repair of the body tissue. For example, about one-fifth of the fowl's body is composed of proteins and such parts as the muscles, skin, feathers and internal organs consist mainly of these substances. The egg also contains approximately 12 per cent of protein—mainly in the white. A constant supply of this nutrient is essential if good health and egg production is to continue. Fish or meat meal with dried yeast are potent sources of protein in a poultry ration, although cereals such as wheat, maize, oats, etc., also contain a certain amount. Tests with fowls have shown that the various sources of protein vary in their efficiency and the following abbreviated table indicates the

relative merits of the different feeding stuffs:—

Biological value of protein feeding stuffs

Taking caseinogen from milk as a basis of 100.0

Fish Meal has an efficiency of 85.3
Meat Meal (Fat Free)   74.1
Wheat Germ   68.0
Meat Meal   62.8
Dried Yeast   62.0
Soya Bean   55.6
Blood Meal   48.0
Split Peas   45.0
Bean Meal   36.3
Grass Meal   22.0
Lentils   19.0

89. The poultry farmer who can obtain supplies of skimmed or sour milk is indeed fortunate. This is a very valuable protein. If the stock is given a mixture of 50 per cent milk and 50 per cent water to drink it will obtain sufficient protein to support both good health and a relatively high egg production figure even though there may be little or no protein in the mash. Some form of milk is, in fact, essential in a chick rearing diet and commercially it is the practice to add 2½ per cent—5 per cent dried milk to the mash.

90. It has been found that some form of animal protein is desirable in the layers' diet and for this reason it is not recommended that the protein part of the mash should consist entirely of vegetable sources such as soya bean, pea or bean meal, etc. Care is also needed when using blood meal. Although this has a high protein content it is very unpalatable to the stock and generally speaking not more than 3 per cent by weight should be added to the ration. Fresh slaughter-house blood can be used and about 1¼ gallons of blood per 100 lbs. of mash will give approximately the correct proportion. It is best to use it clotted and to do this pour into a closely woven bag and cook thoroughly in boiling water. When done the blood will form a solid mass that can be crumbled up for easy mixing.

91. For the small scale and domestic poultry keeper fish waste and horse flesh form a valuable source of protein. These products should be cooked and then minced before

adding to the mash. An allowance of ¾ to 1 oz. per bird a day should be sufficient to balance up the usual waste material. In some districts it is now possible to buy a dehydrated form of horseflesh and this is extremely useful. It should be soaked in boiling water for several hours before use. The advantage of this is that the meat can be kept in stock for long periods without deterioration.

Carbohydrates

92. These supply the energy required by the fowl and make up the bulk of the diet. Wheat, oats, barley, maize and potatoes are rich in carbohydrate and some or all of these products are usually incorporated in the ration. Many other plants also contain large quantities of energy producing foods but there is need for caution when using certain of the by-products now on the market. Woody fibre and cellulose—although chemically carbohydrates—are of little value in poultry nutrition as these substances are not very soluble and the birds cannot extract much nourishment from them. The use of oat husk meal and similar milling products is therefore of limited value in the preparation of a suitable mash for either growing or laying birds. At their best these and similar products can be classed merely as "fillers" suitable only as a drying medium in a mash comprising large quantities of cooked potatoes, etc.

93. Do not be tempted to add more than 5 per cent of these materials, as too much fibre in the diet will cause severe digestive disorders especially in young birds.

94. Potatoes are a valuable source of carbohydrate particularly when the more usual feeding stuffs are scarce. They have been used with success in every type of poultry ration—from that of day-old chicks to the laying hen. There are, however, several points to bear in mind when incorporating potatoes in the mash. In the first place they should be boiled and mashed before being mixed with the rest of the ingredients. Although uncooked potatoes can be used, various tests have proved that the stock can derive far more nourishment from them if the starch grains have been broken down by cooking. It therefore follows that it is uneconomic to feed them in the raw state. Secondly it should be remembered that potatoes

contain a high proportion of water. On a feeding value basis it is usual to use 4 lbs. of potatoes to replace 1 lb. of ordinary meal.

Fats

95. The fats and oils in the diet play very much the same part in animal nutrition as the carbohydrates. They are energy foods. A certain proportion is essential for normal body activity but it is unnecessary to add any additional fat or oil to the average ration as there is a small quantity—about 2 per cent—4 per cent—present in such cereals as wheat, oats, etc. (The use of cod liver oil in a mash is mainly to provide vitamins not oil.)

Vitamins

96. These substances have recently assumed considerable importance in all forms of nutrition. Actually they have always been needed but during the last twenty-five years we have been made more conscious of the vital part they play in good health. Fortunately there is no need for the poultry keeper to worry unduly about these essential food substances as apart from vitamins A and D there is little risk of deficiency. Birds kept on a good varied diet will, in normal circumstances be able to obtain ample supplies of most of the vitamins except the two already mentioned. As the addition of 1 per cent veterinary cod liver oil in the mash will effectively supply vitamins A and D, the poultryman can dismiss the problem from his mind unless he encounters symptoms of the vitamin deficiency diseases. The following table enumerates some of the more useful sources of vitamins and may assist the poultryman when making up a ration.

97. Some deficiency of one or more of these substances will give rise to certain characteristic symptoms and the keen poultryman should keep these signs of poor health in his mind—particularly the following:—

A lack of Vitamin A

98. This will be noticed in young chicks from about three weeks onwards. The birds will stop growing, the feathers will be ruffled and there is general unthriftiness with the eyelids glued together. In adult stock there is a discharge from the

Some Sources of Vitamins

Vitamin A ..	Excellent	..	Cod Liver Oil	
	Very Good	..	Egg-yolk Alfalfa Spinach	Butter Fat Yellow Carrots
	Good ..	..	Liver Whole Milk Clover	Kidney Maize-yellow Pasture Grass
Vitamin B ..	Excellent	..	Yeast	
	Very Good	..	Egg-yolk Maize Germ Cereal grains	Wheat Germ Wheat Bran
	Good ..	..	Buttermilk Liver Potatoes Lettuce	Skim Milk Kidney Kale Rape
Vitamin C ..	Excellent	..	Cabbage Spinach	Lettuce
	Good ..	..	Carrots Turnips	Potatoes
Vitamin D ..	Excellent	..	Cod Liver Oil Sardine Oil Direct sunlight is the most potent agent and usually the best	
	Very Good	..	Egg-yolk	
Vitamin E ..	Excellent	..	Wheat Germ Oil	
	Very Good	..	Wheat Germ Spinach	Lettuce
	Good ..	..	Alfalfa Cotton Seed Oil	Whole Grains Meat Products
Riboflavin ..	Excellent	..	Liver	Yeast
	Very Good	..	Milk	Alfalfa
	Good ..	..	Green Leafy Foods	

eyes and nostrils, and upon examination creamy coloured
pustules will be found in the throat and mouth.

Insufficient Vitamin D

99. Insufficient vitamin D in the diet in the absence of
direct sunlight will bring on an attack of rickets more frequently referred to by poultry keepers as "leg weakness."
The beak often becomes soft and rubbery and the breast bone
may be twisted or otherwise deformed. With layers, thin
shelled eggs are often the first sign of lack of this vitamin.
If neglected, the layers will also exhibit very much the same
leg symptoms (there is a tendency to squat on the ground).
Apart from this egg production will fall and may cease
entirely.

Minerals

100 The position regarding minerals is very much the same
as with vitamins. Small quantities of certain minerals are
absolutely essential to poultry, but with the usual diets
there is little need to worry much about deficiencies. Those
mainly required are phosphorus, sodium, potassium, calcium,
chlorine and magnesium. Foods of plant origin (wheat, oats,
maize, etc.) are reasonably well supplied with magnesium,
phosphorus and potassium but have little sodium and chlorine.
The animal feeding stuffs—meat, fish meal, and milk—contain
most of the minerals needed.

101. When there is a shortage of animal feeding stuffs in
the ration it is advisable to add about ½ per cent common salt.
The use of complex mineral supplements is certainly not
advised when feeding a good quality mash, but there is a use
for such preparations when the diet is made up of large
proportions of unrationed materials. A simple yet efficient
mineral mixture can be made from equal quantities of steamed
bone flour, salt and ground limestone. This is added to the
mash at the rate of 2 per cent.

102. Particular mention must be made of calcium for the
laying stock. An egg shell contains about 2 grammes of
calcium and this mineral must be supplied in sufficient

quantity to ensure that there is ample available to support a high rate of egg production. Many complaints of shell-less or thin shelled eggs arise because the birds are kept short of this substance. It should be a fundamental part of flock management always to have in the pens a hopper of "shell" or limestone grit so that the birds can help themselves. This is better than adding limestone flour to the mash as each bird's requirements differ according to the rate of laying. Another important factor in the production of eggs with good shells is ample vitamin D in the diet. Birds cannot assimulate calcium properly unless this vitamin is present. If therefore the birds are kept intensively (and for all stock in winter) the daily addition of cod liver oil is a prime consideration in obtaining good shell texture.

103. The foregoing brief outline of nutritional theory should enable the intending poultry keeper to tackle the problem of making up a suitable ration for his flock. For those who wish to study the theory of feeding more closely it is recommended that they obtain a copy of the Ministry of Agriculture Bulletin, No. 7, "The Scientific Principles of Poultry Feeding," published by the Stationery Office at 2/-. This bulletin contains a great deal of useful information, and every poultry keeper ought to have a copy. Another useful publication by the Ministry of Agriculture is Bulletin No. 124 "The Composition and Nutritive Value of Feeding Stuffs," price 6d. This little booklet gives analysis figures of the commonly used poultry feeding stuffs and enables the poultry-man to "balance" his mashes with considerable accuracy.

Economy in the Use of Food

104. As feeding stuffs are now so expensive, every endeavour should be made to feed your stock so that every pound of mash is used to the maximum advantage. This does not infer that the birds should be underfed but that they are given just sufficient to enable them to live and lay. A daily allowance ot 5–5½ ozs. (dry weight) of correctly balanced food is adequate for most birds in lay. During periods of very heavy production this quantity can be increased by ½ to 1 oz. Moulting hens and other birds not laying can have the ration reduced to 4 ozs.

per day. Actually, the average bird needs about 2½ ozs. of food just to keep alive. This minimum quantity is essential to the maintenance of life and before any eggs are produced this need must be met. The amount of food consumed over and above this level is available for egg production or growth. The value of adjusting the allowance according to the level of egg production is therefore sound husbandry but needs some considerable experience and skill before it can be applied with the maximum efficiency.

Suggested Rations

105. During rationing domestic poultry keepers were introduced to Balancer Meal which was used in conjunction with household scraps, etc. Up to 8/10 ozs. of these scraps and 2 ozs. of balancer meal were needed per bird daily to produce a diet suitable for egg production. This Balancer Meal is still available and no doubt many small poultry keepers who wish to utilise household waste will continue to buy it instead of ready prepared laying mashes. Where sufficient scraps are available to keep three or four birds going this saving will considerably cheapen the cost of producing home eggs. The question of suitable "domestic" mashes is dealt with later in this chapter, but in the meantime a few examples of normal poultry diets are given. A study of these will show the essential structure of a good all round ration especially if the comments regarding substitution are borne in mind. At all times it should be remembered that a particular ingredient is seldom added to a mash just because it is that particular product. It is included because it supplies certain nutrients required by the birds. It frequently happens that other feeding stuffs are just as suitable and can be used in place of the original when available or price warrants a change.

106. The two recommended rations were designed before the war and are extremely good and in fact would be a little too expensive for most poultry keepers to-day. Even before the war some poultrymen considered that, if anything, the chick rations outlined were too good and that it was desirable to include more bran and less protein-rich foods in order to reduce the rate of growth. They have been quoted, however, to illustrate what a first-class poultry ration should be.

Recommended Ration No. 1 (All Mash Ration)

(Taken from Ministry of Agriculture and Fisheries Bulletin No. 7)
(By kind permission of H.M. Stationery Office)

PARTS BY WEIGHT

Foodstuff	Chick Mash to 8 weeks	Growers Mash 12 weeks on	Layers	Remarks
				All Mash Ration
Maize Meal ..	33	45	45	
Linseed Meal ..	3	3	—	
Bran	14	10	10	
Weatings ..	23	20	26	
Sussex Ground Oats ..	5	14	10	Suitable for intensive systems.
Dried Skim Milk ..	7	—	—	Oyster shell or limestone grit should be given in separate hoppers. So also should insoluble grit. Change over from "Chick" to "Growers" should extend over four weeks.
Fish Meal* ..	7	6½	7½	
Dried Yeast ..	3	—	—	
Limestone Flour ..	2¼	½	½	
Salt	⅝	½	½	
Ferric Oxide ..	⅛	—	—	
Cod Liver Oil ..	2	1	1	

*Or Meat and Bone Meal

Recommended Ration No. 2 (Mash and Grain)

(Taken from Ministry of Agriculture and Fisheries Bulletin No. 7)

(By kind permission of H.M. Stationery office)

PARTS BY WEIGHT

Foodstuff	Chick Mash to 8 weeks	Growers Mash 12 weeks on	Layers	Breeders	Remarks
Maize Meal ..	33	35	22½	22½	For Breeders and Layers approximate 2 ozs. per day of 3 pts. wheat, 2 pts. maize.
Linseed Meal ..	3	3	—	—	
Bran	14	15	15	15	
Weatings ..	23	26	40	40	
S.G. Oats ..	5	10	10	10	Chicks are fed on cut wheat from four weeks spread on mash and get on to adult grain mixture by fifteen weeks.
Dried Skim Milk	7	—	—	—	
Fish Meal* ..	7	7	12½	8	
Dried Yeast ..	3	2½	—	2½	
Limestone Flour ..	2¼	—	—	—	
Salt	⅝	½	—	—	Other comments same as for "All Mash" Ration.
Ferric Oxide ..	⅛	—	—	—	
Cod Liver Oil ..	2	1	—	2	

*Or Meat and Bone Meal

Recommended Rations No. 3 (Standard Formulæ)

Foodstuff	Rearing		Growers	Layers		Breeders	Fattening		Battery
	Int.	F.R.		Int.	F.R.		Sus.	Coun.	
Weatings ..	35	35	30	35	35	30	—	30	25
Bran ..	10	20	30	10	20	20	—	—	35
Maize Meal ..	20	20	22	25	25	25	—	30	12½
S.G. Oats ..	10	10	10	10	10	10	13	30	12½
Fish Meal ..	7½	7½	8	10	10	5	—	5	5
Grass Meal ..	10	—	—	10	—	—	—	—	10
Dried Yeast ..	—	—	—	—	—	2½	—	—	—
Dried Milk ..	5	5	—	—	—	5	1	5	—
Salt ..	1	1	—	—	—	1	—	—	½
Cod Liver Oil ..	1½	1	—	1	—	1	—	—	1

PARTS BY WEIGHT

Int. — Intensive. F.R. — Free Range. Sus. — Sussex. Coun. — Country

NOTE : A. Meat and Bone Meal could be used to replace Fish Meal.
     B. With the exception of the Fattening and Battery rations the formulae suggested are for use with the usual grain feed daily.
     C. Bran and Weatings are now sold mixed as Millers Offals.

107. The good commercial rations outlined in Recommended Rations No. 3 are simple and could be used as a suitable standard from which to compile rations on the farm according to availability of supplies.

108. There can be considerable latitude with regard to the actual ingredients. For example the maize meal could be replaced by ground barley or coarsely ground wheat. Grass meal is now the usual substitute for Alfalfa Meal. Sour milk could be given in place of the dried skim milk. Many farmers also incorporate "pudding" (processed household waste) or potatoes to replace some of the cereals. A similar use can also be made of acorns and artichokes. With the former it is not advisable to feed more than 1 oz. per bird a day or there may be some constipation among the stock. An excess will also cause discolouration of the egg yolk. Artichokes are best used in the same way as potatoes but owing to the nature of the carbohydrate it is better to store them until February. Dried brewers' grains are also a substitute for cereals if limited to about 10/15 per cent of the total ration. Bean meal can be used to replace part of the fish or meat meal. When this is done it is desirable to add one part mineral mixture to every five parts bean meal.

109. Sunflower seeds form excellent substitutes for the normal grain feed. These contain at least as much feeding valne as wheat and also considerably more protein. It would well repay the small poultry keeper to cultivate this plant on odd patches of otherwise waste land as the seed will form a valuable addition to the layers' diet.

110. A very useful but expensive protein foodstuff is dried yeast, but it is well worth while as a replacement for part of the fish or meat meal in chick rations as it also contains valuable vitamins essential to growth. The high cost, however, makes it too dear to use in the layers' diet.

111. The most important consideration when using substitute feeds is to restrict the quantity and to vary the diet as much as possible. As a safeguard it is best to introduce gradually any new food. Begin by adding $2\frac{1}{2}$ per cent and if the birds are not adversely affected then slowly increase the amount to about 10 per cent.

Home Prepared Rations

112. During the period of rationing some very extraordinary diets were made by poultry farmers in order to keep their businesses going. These very bulky and often expensive diets were, quite frankly, inefficient, but they were better than no food

at all. Now that we are back to normal buying facilities it is far better for the smaller poultry farmer and the domestic poultry keeper to buy ready prepared meals for such purposes as chick rearing. Chick mashes need careful planning and it is not easy even to-day to obtain regular supplies of some ingredients of high quality. Unless, therefore, you have the time to spend searching for the special items, buy a proprietary chick mash or pellets.

113. For those people such as caterers who have access to large quantities of waste materials the following rations have been used successfully:—

> 80 lbs. Cooked Potatoes
> 20 lbs. Millers Offals
> 3 lbs. Fish Meal (or Meat Meal)
> 2 lbs. Dried Yeast
> 5 lbs. Limestone Flour
> 2 Pints Cod Liver Oil

This is fed as a wet mash and good results have been reported from its use. Owing to its bulkiness the rate of growth is not so good as with a normal chick ration. If the stock can be given some milk to drink the results should be better.

114. To follow on the above chick ration a suitable fattening mash for birds intended for table would be as under. This is suitable from about eight weeks to killing.

> 20 lbs. Cooked Potatoes
> 20 lbs. Bakery Waste
> 30 lbs. Kitchen Waste
> 20 lbs. Meat or Fish Scraps
> 10 ozs. Salt

115. Layers diets, during recent years, have been many and varied and the formulae which follow have, from time to time, been recommended by various authorities in the Poultry press. These have the advantage that the usual rationed foods were considerably reduced. Very high egg production cannot be expected with these mashes as there is little doubt that the hen does best when fed on a concentrated diet. The large amounts of food necessary when using bulky and watery materials places a great strain on the digestive system and in any case the fowl is often unable to consume sufficient to

make high egg yields possible. Nevertheless such substitute diets enabled the poultry farmer to eke out the small official rations and on this basis were worth consideration.

116. **Layers' Economy Ration No. 1**

> 4 parts Cooked Potatoes
> 4 parts Layers' Meal
> ½ part Dried Grass Meal
> ½ part Dried Yeast
> (8 ozs. Approx. per bird daily)

117. **Layers' Economy Ration No. 2**

> 50 lbs. Layers' Meal
> 35 lbs. Biscuit Meal
> 10 lbs. Grass Meal
> 5 lbs. Fish/Meat Meal
> ½ pint Cod Liver Oil

The biscuit meal should be soaked for twelve hours before using.

118.   Apart from using ready prepared layers' meals there are many possible diets for use by the domestic poultryman. Practically every small poultry keeper has a different mash based on the materials he can obtain. The following are typical and form a sound basis on which to work.

No. 1

> 3 ozs. Balancer Meal
> 3 ozs. Mashed Potatoes   ⎫
> 1 oz. Bread or Bakery Waste   ⎬ per bird daily
> ½ Teaspoon Cod Liver Oil   ⎭
> ¼ oz. Green Stuff

No. 2

> 2 ozs. Balancer Meal   ⎫
> 8 ozs. Household Scraps   ⎬ per bird daily
> 2¼ ozs. Wilted and Chopped Nettles ⎭

No. 3

> 3 parts Balancer Meal
> 6 parts Cooked Potatoes
> 1 part Dried Food Waste

No. 4

3 parts Balancer Meal
5 parts Cooked Potatoes
1 part Dried Food Waste
½ part Grass Meal

119. Undoubtedly the cheapest plan for the domestic poultry keeper is to give each layer 2½—3 ozs. of a balancer meal per day plus about 6/7 ozs. of household scraps. The actual amount of scraps given will depend largely on the quality of the material used. Layers cannot produce eggs in any quantity on a poor diet of potato peelings and cabbage leaves, so if the scraps available are of this type, you must provide extra protein and starchy foods. 1 oz. of meat or fish scraps plus 4/5 ozs. of some form of cereal must be allowed for each layer kept. For those who live in the country where they can allow their birds to roam on comparatively extensive range, a small daily allowance of a balancer meal (say 3/3½ ozs.) is adequate during the spring and summer months as the stock will pick up the remainder of their diet from the ground. However, when birds are kept intensively and only a few good quality household scraps are available it is certainly better now that rationing is over to buy a ready-made intensive layers' food as this is correctly balanced and will prove the cheapest in the long run.

120. The position is, of course, somewhat different for the larger household where household scraps are plentiful. The various scraps should be kept separate. Meat, fish, cheese rinds, sour milk, etc., are protein rich substances, whereas stale bread, pastry, potato peelings are valuable sources of carbohydrate. Cabbage leaves and similar items have little actual feeding value but supply vitamins and minerals.

121. Meat and fish scraps should be put through a mincer after cooking. The odd pieces of cake, etc., should be dried slowly in an oven and then crumbled into a fine meal. This latter helps to dry off the other plate scrapings and keeps the finished mash reasonably dry. Green vegetables should be minced or chopped and added raw as cooking destroys some of the vitamins. Incidentally, lawn clippings are greatly appreciated by poultry. Either feed them fresh, or dry in the

sun and store for winter use when they help to replace grass meal. The more the diet can be varied the better will be the result, as when numerous types of food are given there is less risk of a deficiency of any one nutrient.

Balancing the Diet

122.   The theory underlying the compilation of a good balanced diet is, in the main, quite simple. On a dry weight basis the correct proportion of protein to carbohydrate is obtained when the stock is fed a ration of mixed cereal grains and their by-products plus a 10 per cent allowance of good quality fish or meat meal. During times of scarcity this should be kept in mind and when feeding the stock try to work to this proportion. It will help to remember that such things as potatoes are at least 75 per cent water, and that ordinary meat and fish scraps at least 50 per cent. Bread and pastry scraps also contain quite a proportion of water and this is the reason for drying them in the oven before use. On a dry weight basis the birds need at least 4½-5 ozs. of food daily.

Food Intake During Growth

123.   For the larger poultry keeper the following figures of food consumption during the growing period may be of interest. The quantities stated are approximate and in any case are based on good quality pre-war feeding stuffs. It has been found by many commercial poultry farmers that there is a tendency for the amounts required to be exceeded and an allowance of 25 per cent—33 per cent may not be too high in many instances.

Table 1

Food Consumption from Day-old to Maturity
(100 birds)

Week	Per 100 Chicks	Cumulative figure
1st	10 lbs.	10 lbs.
2nd	20 lbs.	30 lbs.
3rd	30 lbs.	60 lbs.

Table 1 (*continued*)

Food Consumption from Day-Old to Maturity (100 birds)

Week	Per 100 Chicks	Cumulative figure
4th	40 lbs.	100 lbs.
5th	50 lbs.	150 lbs.
6th	60 lbs.	210 lbs.
7th	70 lbs.	280 lbs.
8th	80 lbs.	360 lbs.
9th	90 lbs.	4 cwts.
10th	100 lbs.	5 cwts.
11th	105 lbs.	6 cwts.
12th	110 lbs.	6¾ cwts.
13th	115 lbs.	7¾ cwts.
14th	120 lbs.	8¾ cwts.
15th	125 lbs.	10 cwts.
16th	130 lbs.	11¼ cwts.
17th	135 lbs.	12½ cwts.
18th	140 lbs.	13¾ cwts.
19th	145 lbs.	15 cwts.
20th	150 lbs.	16¼ cwts.
21st	155 lbs.	17¾ cwts.
22nd	160 lbs.	19 cwts.
23rd	165 lbs.	20½ cwts.
24th	170 lbs.	1 ton, 2 cwts.

124. Average pre-war figures of food consumption for laying birds are quoted in Table 2. The same remarks regarding present day increases apply owing to the rather bulkier food now available to the poultry farmer.

Table 2

Food Consumption (Per Year) Layers

Birds in Laying Batteries   105/110 lbs. per bird
Birds on free range   96 lbs. per bird

plus a supplement of approximately 5 lbs. of limestone grit or flour per bird.

125. When producing birds for the table the following figures indicate the desirability of securing rapid early weight gains as an increased quantity of food is required as the age advances.

Food Consumption per lb. Gain in Weight

0— 8 weeks	...	$3\frac{1}{2}$ lbs. approximately
8—16 weeks	...	$5\frac{3}{4}$ lbs. approximately
16—22 weeks	...	9 lbs. approximately

Feeding Times

126. A final word on the question of feeding times may not be out of place. There is no hard and fast rule about this, but general commercial practice is to feed twice a day— the first feed being in the morning and the second during the afternoon. It is the opinion of many skilled poultrymen that although the actual time of feeding is unimportant it does help if the birds are fed regularly. For instance, it is not considered good management to give the afternoon feed one day at 3 o'clock and at 5 o'clock the next. If regular hours are kept the stock soon settles down to the routine and tends to be more contented. Contented stock—as any husbandman will tell you—always does much better than restless animals, so there is possibly quite a lot to be said for regular meal times.

CHAPTER IV

BREEDING

Selecting the Breeders

127. Upon the soundness of the breeding programme
depends the future health and productive ability of the
poultry flock. In fact it is safe to say that unless the parent
stock is chosen with great care for the task ahead of them
there will be a gradual loss of stamina, a greater incidence of
disease and a marked reduction in the number of eggs laid
by each succeeding year's birds.

128. During the past thirty years a good deal of work
has been done both by practical breeders and research
workers towards raising the egg production of the domestic
fowl. Many "barn-door" poultry flocks in the past did not
average more than eighty/ninety eggs per bird annually and
the bulk of these were laid in the spring and early summer.
The average is now nearer 140/150 eggs per bird. This
improvement is the result of a number of factors. Better
feeding, housing and management have contributed much,
but so has selection of the breeding stock. It is futile to expect
to create a first-class laying flock from poor quality parents.
The mere introduction of a male into a pen of hens is certainly
not breeding in the true sense of the word.

Health and Stamina

129 Probably the most important factor to be considered
when selecting the birds for the breeding pen is that of health
and stamina. There is little sense in choosing a female on the
basis of her first year's egg production only. She may be a good
layer but if she is undersized or lacks stamina there is a very
good chance that she will produce mediocre chicks which
grow into weaklings possessing neither the ability to lay nor
even to live.

Judging the Stock

130. Constitutional vigour can be judged to some extent
from external appearances. The alert, active, deep bodied

and bright eyed bird is more likely to be fit and have the ability to pass on the factor of good health to her chicks than the sluggish or under-sized specimen. A good time to judge a female is at the end of her first laying season. If she moults late in the year (September-October), is reasonably plump and has the above-mentioned characteristics then she should possess stamina and good health. Do not be misled by a ragged appearance. The good layer often has worn feathers at the end of the laying season. This applies particularly when a male bird is in the pen. The fine immaculate female with every feather in place should be suspect. Quite likely she has moulted early and has contributed little to the daily egg production.

Progeny Testing

131. Unfortunately, however, repeated tests have proved that there is no certainty about breeding on external appearances only. It is a common experience to find that the best looking birds in the flock prove disappointing as breeders. The only real criterion of a bird's value as a breeder is a test of that bird's offspring. If the chicks do well during rearing and later in life prove good layers then it is safe to assume that the parents have in their make-up the characteristics necessary for good health and high egg production.

132. Needless to say very few birds can pass this test. Some may possess the factors for good health at the expense of egg production. They may give chicks that will live and grow to maturity with low mortality but the average number of eggs laid by them may be comparatively low. On the other hand it is often found that other breeders have a comparatively high proportion of losses in their chicks but those that do live may be excellent layers.

133. A word of warning is necessary at this stage. Although the necessity for an economic rate of egg production must be kept in sight too much importance should not be placed on this one factor alone. In my own opinion health should come first. There is little profit or pleasure in owning a flock with a high death rate however well the birds may lay as individuals. It therefore follows that it is important to select the breeding stock first on the basis of health and secondly on productive ability as shown during the pullet year.

134. Having built up a sound fit flock of birds the question of improving egg production can be tackled on safer ground than is the case if too much emphasis is placed on the egg record to the detriment of livability. It is much easier to step up the rate of laying in a healthy flock than to decrease the death rate in a group of birds lacking the essential constitutional vigour.

Selection by Families

135. It is generally found that the characteristics for good or poor health runs in families, and any sound breeding programme should be based on the family records rather than on the performance of the individual bird. To a certain extent this makes the breeder's task easier. With a suitable division of his flock he can ascertain which group of birds is giving the best results and he can concentrate on using that particular group for his future breeding operations.

136. However, the selection of the breeding flock on such lines, while sound, must of necessity be limited to the larger poultry enterprises. The small breeder cannot usually run on enough chicks to make the test reliable. He must therefore work on more ordinary lines. The selection of the breeding stock can be, and in many cases is done on the basis of handling and observation. The external characteristics indicative of good health and a high potential egg yield can be summed up as follows:—

Head Points

137. The comb and wattles should be well developed, bright red and velvety to the touch. Eyes should be bright and prominent. Avoid the sunken-eyed bird as she is often a poor layer and may enjoy only indifferent health. A good stout beak is another indication of stamina.

Plumage

138. Choose birds with "tight" feathering. It is a good sign when the feathers are carried close to the body and spring back into position when stroked the wrong way. "Loose" feathering shows lack of vitality and often indicates early moulting. There is considerable controversy on the question of feather colour and markings. Many breeders contend that some consideration should be given to the maintenance of the

breed characteristics and reject from the breeding pens any birds not typical in regard to the feather colour or markings. Others pay little attention to this factor and argue that they are breeding for economic and not show standard qualities. If, for example, you are in business as a breeder of Rhode Island Red poultry then customers will expect to receive birds that look like Rhode Island Reds. Any great departure from the normal breed standard may result in loss of business. On the other hand many commercial egg producers care little for appearances. They want a bird that will live and lay, and show a profit over the cost of food, etc.

139. It seems wise, therefore, to adopt a middle course. Reject those birds that are badly mismarked but do not adopt an extremist attitude. Small colour defects should be overlooked, and a really first-class bird should never be rejected because of plumage. If she has proved herself as a layer use her in the breeding pen as 99 per cent of poultry keepers want eggs not beautiful feathers.

Carriage

140. The way in which a bird carries itself also gives valuable information about health and fitness. The wings should be close to the body and the tail carried well up. An active disposition is a good sign. The bird that is constantly scratching and is inquisitive is usually healthy. Suspect those that stand about in the run and evince little interest in what is going on.

Body Points

141. Good health shows itself in practically every part of the body. Choose those birds with wide bodies, plump breasts, full abdomens and stout shanks as these points are associated with vigour. The narrow-backed, pinched up bird with spindly legs is not fit to produce future layers.

Pullets or Hens?

142. For some time now there has been considerable discussion amongst poultrymen regarding the relative merits of using pullets (birds in their first laying year) as opposed to hens (birds in the second or subsequent laying season). Generally speaking the use of pullets for breeding has been

condemned on the basis that you are introducing an un-
known quantity into the programme. It is not known whether
a pullet has the ability to live through her first year. Certainly
on this basis there is some justification for the criticism of
using pullets as breeders. There is, however, apart from this
factor—admitted a big one—no real justification for barring
the use of pullets for breeding. A well developed pullet will
give as good offspring during her first year as she will later on
in her life. The snag is—as already said—that birds may be
bred from parents that will die at a comparatively early age
and this inherited weakness may be passed on to the next
generation. The small man who cannot afford to keep a large
number of birds would do better to play for safety and use
only hens in his breeding flocks. If, however, he can scrap the
progeny of a pullet that dies during its first season then there
is no reason why pullets should not be used in the breeding pen.
Their higher egg production and better hatchability are important economic considerations. Also the fact that a whole
year will be saved means that it will be known more quickly
whether the breeding programme is working out according to
plan.

Selecting the Male

143. The importance of selecting a good male bird to head
the breeding pen cannot be too strongly emphasized. The
inclusion of one poor quality female will have much less
affect on the future of the flock than the use of a mediocre
male. If the male is a failure then there is a chance that all
the progeny will be affected whereas in the case of the female
only her sons and daughters will be involved.

144. If you cannot adopt one of the progeny testing schemes
then select males on health and vigour. When using cockerels
(first year birds) be sure that they are fully mature before
placing them with the females. Males are rarely fully developed
until nine or ten months old.

145. A very interesting and helpful booklet on the selection
of birds has been prepared by the Ministry of Agriculture.
It is Bulletin No. 59 entitled "The Culling of Poultry" published by the Stationery Office at 9d. Every small-scale poultry
keeper should get a copy as it is an excellent guide in assessing
the value of a flock of domestic birds.

Ratio of Males to Females

146. The number of females with which a male can be mated depends mainly on the vigour of the bird concerned. A good vigorous cockerel should be able to fertilize the eggs from about fifteen/twenty birds, particularly the light breeds such as leghorns, etc. With the heavier breeds allow one male to twelve/fifteen females. A particular point to watch with cocks (males in their second year) is that their spurs are kept short otherwise the backs of the females may be severely torn. The long pointed spurs can be trimmed down with a pair of bone forceps or pruning shears and then a red hot iron applied to stop bleeding. Another method is to force a hot potato on the spur. After three or four minutes the horn will be softened and can be removed by twisting.

Saving Eggs

147. Eggs from mated birds can be saved for hatching about five/seven days after the male has been placed in the breeding pen. If the male dies or is removed for some reason and a fresh male is introduced into the pen it is safe to assume that he will have supplanted the original sire within about one week, and the eggs will have been fertilised by the new-comer.

Checking for fertility

148. It is a good plan to check the male for fertility before the breeding season begins as fertility is an individual characteristic. A few eggs should be incubated for seven to ten days. If the bulk of these are fertile then the male is doing his job properly. The value of this check test is well worth the sacrifice of the few eggs involved, as an infertile male will waste a lot of time and eggs just when the loss can be afforded least.

Dubbing

149. Apart from sterility there are several factors which can affect fertility. Very cold weather and strong winds will play havoc with breeding flocks. This applies to all birds but particularly so with the light breeds which have large combs and wattles. It is therefore desirable to provide the birds with some means of protection. Hessian screens placed

(A) A flock of Rhode Island Red hens on a commercial breeding farm. This illustrates the general layout of a free range poultry farm

(B) The semi-intensive system employed by many pedigree breeders. It comprises small fixed pens often equipped with alternative runs to maintain the land in reasonable condition. While one run is being used the other is rested

PLATE III

(**A**) The ridge board illustrated provides efficient extraction of stale air without down draughts

(**B**) The wrong type of ridge capping. This inverted " V " style frequently gives rise to severe down draughts which may adversely affect the health and production of the flock

(**C**) Apex type night arks in use on a large poultry farm

PLATE IV

(A) A good type Rhode Island Red Pullet. Note the great depth of body, sturdy beak and legs and bold prominent eye. All these factors are indications of good health and stamina. A bird such as this is worth a place in the breeding pen

(B) A poor type Rhode Island Red Pullet. The cutaway body and general slightness of the bird may be regarded as signs of weakness. Although she may give quite a good account of herself as a layer her use as a breeder should be avoided

PLATE V

(**A**) Broody coop for natural rearing

(**B**) A suitable water container for a batch of chicks.   To prevent a damp patch on the litter the fount should be stood on a platform

(**C**) A modern " Swing-bar " food trough that prevents waste and contamination. The chicks have ample room to peck at the food but cannot dust bath in it.   Neither can they foul the contents with their droppings

PLATE VI

to break the force of the north and east winds will help, but in exposed locations it is best to dub the males. Dubbing consists of removing the comb to prevent frost-bite. It is quite a simple operation and is much less painful to the bird than the effect of a frozen comb. The bird's head should be held firmly against a flat piece of wood and the comb removed with one firm cut with a very sharp knife or razor blade. Make the cut about ¼ in. from the head. To check bleeding run cold water over the wound and then dress with Friars Balsam. This operation will result in considerably better fertility especially if the stock is kept on range in the colder parts of the country.

150. An alternative, but not so effective precaution against frost-bite, is to apply petroleum jelly to the males' combs. This will help the birds to a certain extent, but will not be sufficient protection in really severe weather. In any case, where there is a risk of frost, it is necessary to repeat the application every two/three weeks.

Cross Breeding and Sex Linkage

151. For many commercial purposes such as egg production or table birds it is not essential to have pure breeds, and a large number of cross-bred birds are now produced annually. Cross-breeding consists of mating two different breeds together. It results, if good quality parent stock is used, in increased vigour. When certain breeds are employed it is possible to detect the sex of the chicks when they are hatched and this means considerable saving in food—it not being necessary to run on the surplus males until their sex would normally be obvious.

152. For the smaller poultry keeper who would otherwise have to employ the services of a professional chick sexer this system of cross breeding is invaluable. It is based on the fact that the female passes on certain characteristics to her sons which she does not transmit to her daughters. The genetical aspect of this factor need not concern us here but its practical application is as follows.

153. There are three sex-linked factors of value commercially. The first is based on the fact that when a male with "gold" plumage is mated to "silver" plumed females the resulting chicks will have either gold or silver down. The

3

female chicks will inherit their father's colour and the cockerel chicks that of their mother. The golden or buff coloured chicks are therefore pullets and the silver or white are males. A popular gold-silver cross is that of the Rhode Island Red Male to Light Sussex Females. The following crosses will also give sex-linkage on this factor:—

Male		Female
Buff Leghorn	X	White Wyandotte or Light Sussex
Buff Minorca	X	White Wyandotte or Light Sussex
Buff Wyandotte	X	White Wyandotte or Light Sussex
Buff Plymouth Rock	X	White Wyandotte or Light Sussex
Brown Leghorn	X	Light Sussex or Columbian Wyandotte
Partridge Wyandotte	X	Light Sussex or Columbian Wyandotte
Golden Laced Wyandotte	X	Light Sussex or Columbian Wyandotte

154. The second characteristic giving rise to sex linkage is the barring found in such breeds as the Barred Plymouth Rock. When certain non-barred breed males are mated to barred females the progeny produced can be sexed by the head spot of the young cockerel chicks. The pullets are black with dark beak and shanks. The cokerels have a light spot on the head with lighter coloured beaks and shanks. The following crosses will give this sex linkage:—

Males		Females
All Black Varieties	X	Barred Plymouth Rocks
Rhode Island Red		Cuckoo Leghorns
Brown Leghorns		Scots Greys
		North Holland Blues

155. The third sex-linked characteristic is the rate of feather growth. The light breeds feather much more rapidly than the heavier breeds. When a rapid feathering male is mated to slow feathering females the progeny can be sexed on the size of the wing feathers immediately after hatching. The pullets will have longer wing feathers than the males. It is essential

to sex the chicks as soon after hatching as possible, and a certain amount of experience is needed to acquire proficiency. The following crosses are sex-linked on this factor:—

Males		Females
White Leghorns		Rhode Island Red
Black Leghorns		Plymouth Rocks (Buff and
Brown Leghorns	X	Barred)
Minorca		White Wyandotte
Ancona		Orpington

This last method of producing sex-linked chicks is not in common use because there is some element of doubt in a certain proportion of the chicks examined. It is therefore not very suitable for the poultryman who wants to sell "guaranteed 95 per cent pullets," but is sufficiently accurate for the small man who cannot afford the food to run the cockerels on till about eight weeks old. By adopting this system he could reject up to at least 80 per cent of the males at hatching time.

Domestic Breeding

156. The domestic poultry keeper who is mainly concerned with producing eggs for his own consumption is certainly not advised to do his own breeding. It is essentially a specialist's job and if hens are kept merely to supply the household with eggs and some meat for the table it is better to buy replacement stock from a breeding farm.

157. But the person who is keen enough to make poultry his hobby can—with attention to detail—get good results. The novice who intends to take up breeding should, as a first step, join the local poultry club. Other enthusiasts will be found there who are only too willing to give good advice.

Show Breeding

158. When breeding on a small scale it is usual to specialise in one of the more ornamental "Show" varieties. Many of these breeds have their own club, and after the intending breeder has decided on his pet variety he will be well advised to join the society catering exclusively for that breed. The handbook issued will tell him all he needs to know about the type, colour and appearance of the birds concerned.

159. Visits to the national and local poultry shows will increase his knowledge of what is required to make a "winner,"

and the club concerned will put him in touch with first-class breeders. A small start should be made by purchasing a good male and two or three females of the selected breed.

160. The first season will teach more than pages of good advice. It will be found, for example, that "like does not always beget like." The offspring from the breeding pen may not be quite so good as the parents. They may show colour variations which preclude the birds from the show bench, or they may not have the ability to live. It will be gradually learnt that in order to produce a good specimen up to the breed standard the good and bad points of the breeding flock must be considered. A female, for instance, that is too small or is too dark in feather colour must be mated to a male that is particularly good in such points. Even this does not automatically produce the prize winner. Things seldom go according to plan when dealing with living creatures.

161. The old hands at the business, keen fanciers who have been breeding winners for years, know a good many "tricks of the trade," and are usually keen to help the interested beginner. Some of the poultry clubs in London and the other big towns have really skilled amateur breeders among their members who regularly win a "first" at the national shows. Knowledge is best gained by contact with such men.

162. Membership of a go-ahead club gives additional zest to the hobby of poultry breeding. Competition between members is keen and in the process of competing valuable knowledge of the numerous small details which go to make perfection is gained.

CHAPTER V

INCUBATION

Artificial Methods

163. A knowledge of the general principles of incubation will enable the poultryman to choose those methods best suited to his particular circumstances. Nowadays the broody hen with her clutch of eggs plays only an infinitesimal part in the production of the many millions of chicks produced annually. Mammoth machines holding anything up to 24,000 eggs are the rule on the larger poultry farms and commercial hatcheries. Even small-scale poultry keepers frequently make use of one of the less ambitious models holding from 30 to 150 eggs at a setting.

164. It would not be possible in a book of this size to describe all the various machines, but it can be assumed that most of those now being offered for sale are efficient and will give good results providing the instructions regarding temperature and humidity are followed faithfully. There are no hard and fast rules applicable to all machines, so it is essential to operate the machine you select in accordance with the maker's recommendations.

Storing Hatching Eggs

165. The basic requirements of good incubation, however, apply to all methods and models. In the first place it is useless to expect a high hatching percentage if stale eggs are set. Under normal conditions of storage eggs may be held for seven/eight days before being placed under the hen or in the incubator. Eggs stored longer than this will give poorer results and may produce less vigorous chicks. Every extra day an egg is held reduces its chance of hatching. Therefore use only fresh eggs.

Storage Conditions

166. The conditions under which the eggs are stored also influences the final hatching figures. The ideal holding

temperature is 50° F. with a safety range varying between
40°F.—65°F. Both chilling and overheating for prolonged
periods will reduce hatchability. The position of eggs during
storage is not of great importance. In the past it was thought
desirable to turn the eggs daily while being stored, but recent
research has proved that providing the eggs are not held
longer than seven/eight days turning does not increase the
percentage hatched.

Selection of Eggs

167.   Another important pre-incubation factor is the selection
of the eggs. Any abnormal eggs should be rejected. Irregular
shaped or thin shelled eggs are undesirable, and so are very
large or very small eggs. The best size is around 2 ozs.—2½ozs.
The continuous use of small eggs will tend to produce a
strain of poultry laying small eggs. Alternatively the use of
very large (3 oz.—4 oz.) eggs is not recommended as they
seldom hatch as well as the normal size. It follows, therefore,
that good shaped eggs with a strong shell texture and of
average size should be set for the best results.

Number of eggs to Set

168.   The number of eggs which it is necessary to set to
produce any given number of birds varies according to the
quality of the breeding stock and the efficiency of the incubator
and its operator. With good quality stock and reasonable
incubation skill it is usual to set four to five eggs for each
laying pullet required. This may sound high, but it should
be borne in mind that approximately 10/15 per cent of the
eggs put into the machine will be infertile and that possibly
another 15/20 per cent will not produce chicks. An average
hatching percentage of 65/70 per cent over the entire season
is the experience of most large poultry farmers. Here and there
you will hear of better results, but taking everything into
consideration if you average 65/70 per cent of all eggs set you
should not be disappointed. With this hatching percentage
six/seven chicks from every ten eggs set can be expected. At
least half of these will be cockerels giving a figure of approximately three pullets hatched. There will almost invariably
be some losses during rearing and even when the pullets
reach maturity a small proportion of them will be unfit for
retention in the laying flock. The allowance of four to five

eggs per adult pullet needed is therefore reasonable for planning purposes.

Hatching Dates

169. The question of hatching dates also requires careful study. Very late hatched birds (May—July) seldom come into production before the severe weather starts with the result that their first year's production (the most profitable) is greatly reduced. Early hatched stock (December—January) on the other hand matures early but often goes into an autumn moult which may be prolonged if the weather is bad. The best time for hatching in order to secure the highest egg yields during the pullet year is March for the heavy breeds (Sussex, Rhode Island Red, Plymouth Rocks, etc.) and mid-March to mid-April for the light breeds (Leghorns, Anconas, etc.). Therefore the eggs for the heavy breeds should be set during the last three weeks in February and the first two weeks in March, and during March for the light-breeds.

Housing the Incubator

170. It is important before starting incubation to provide suitable accommodation for the machine. There is no doubt that the room in which the incubator is placed influences considerably the results obtained. A well ventilated room which maintains a fairly even temperature is best. Violent fluctuations in temperature make it more difficult to secure uniform heat in the incubator—especially with the smaller models. A constant room heat of 60°F.—65°F. is recommended. A cellar, if properly ventilated, is often the best place for small incubators. There must be a regular flow of fresh air through the room otherwise there will be a high proportion of dead-in-shell and "sticky" chicks. This is because the developing embryos are not receiving enough oxygen.

Operating Temperatures

171. The actual temperature at which to run the incubator varies according to the type of machine. The large forced draught machines are normally operated at 100° F., whereas the small natural draught models are generally adjusted to register a temperature of 103° F. for the first ten days, and the remaining period they operate at 104° F.

172. One well-known manufacturer of small incubators recommends the following operating temperatures for hens' eggs. When waterfowl are being incubated it is suggested that the machine be adjusted to give a temperature 2° F. less.

Room Temperature	Incubator Temperature for 1st ten days	Incubator Temperature for remaining period
50°F.	104°F.	105°F.
60°F.	103°F.	104°F.
70°F.	102°F.	103°F.
80°F.	101°F.	102°F.
90°F.	100°F.	101°F.

The reason why higher temperatures are used in the case of the smaller incubator is because the heat is not uniform throughout the depth of the machine. A reading of 103° F.—104° F. taken near the upper side of the eggs gives the correct temperature mid-way between the top and bottom of the eggs. As regards the details of operation—be guided by the makers' suggestions. The various models vary slightly and need a little different handling.

Turning Eggs
173. It is extremely important to turn the eggs while in the incubator. With the large forced draught machine, four—six times daily is generally recommended. In the case of the small incubator where the turning is done by hand the eggs should be turned at least twice a day—three times if possible. The reason for turning is to prevent the embryo adhering to the shell membrane. If the eggs are not turned at all very poor hatching results indeed will be obtained. They should not, however, be turned after the 18th day.

Moisture Requirement
174. The question of moisture required during incubation also affects the results. There is, however, a certain amount of latitude in this matter. Excessive moisture will result in reduced hatchability and the chicks will be too large. On the

other hand, too dry an atmosphere will result in excessive evaporation from the egg with the result that the chicks will be undersized and there will be a high percentage of chicks failing to hatch. With the larger machines a relative humidity of 60 per cent is usually suggested. In the case of natural draught incubators the moisture device incorporated in the design will normally provide the correct degree of humidity.

Testing for Fertility

175. The eggs may be tested for fertility on the seventh day if white shelled, or on the ninth day if tinted. To do this the room is darkened and each egg is placed in front of a strong light. Fertile eggs show a dark spot with thin lines (the blood vessels) extending in all directions. An infertile egg will be clear except for the shadow of the yolk. Some may show a red ring in the yolk. This is caused by the germ dying soon after incubation started. On commercial plants using forced-draught machines testing is usually done on the eighteenth day. This saves the trouble of re-grouping the eggs on the trays as on the same day the eggs are transferred to the hatching compartments.

Incubation Periods

176. The actual hatching takes place on or about the twenty-first day in the case of fowls. The usual incubation periods for the various species of domestic poultry are as follows:—

Fowls	21 days	Geese	30/32 days
Ducks	28 days	Turkeys	28 days
	Guinea Fowls 28/30 days		

Either late or early hatching may result by the operation of the incubator at the incorrect thermometer reading. A uniformally high temperature will decrease the number of days required, and a low one will mean an extra day or so. Both these abnormalities are highly undesirable, and to get strong healthy chicks the machine should be run so that the birds hatch out on the correct day. It is essential to avoid VERY HIGH incubation temperatures as the developing embryo has very little resistance. A rise of five/six degrees above that recommended by the makers will almost invariably result in heavy losses. A low temperature for several hours may not affect the hatch very much although every endeavour should be made to maintain as even a heat in the machine as possible.

Removing Chicks from Machine

177. Do not leave the chicks in the incubator too long after hatching. This applies particularly to the smaller machines where often there is insufficient oxygen. Be careful, however, of placing chicks in the nursery tray provided on some machines. The temperature in this compartment is frequently very much lower than desirable and if the chicks are put into it chilling may take place with consequent heavy losses during the rearing period. Once the chicks have dried they are much better off in chick boxes or in the brooder.

Assisting the Chicks

178. Some beginners adopt the unwise policy of assisting the chicks out of their shells. It should be taken as a rule that if the chick is not strong enough to break out without help then it is not worth helping. The importance of rearing only birds of good stamina and vitality cannot be over-stressed, and in view of this it is strongly suggested that weakly chicks are not helped to hatch.

Judging Day-old Chicks

179. A good chick when dried off after hatching should resemble a ball of fluff. It should feel firm and solid to the touch and should weigh about 1½ ozs. There should be no shell adhering to the down, neither should there be any "stickiness." The strong healthy chick will stand firmly on its legs —any with splayed legs should be killed. Look out for other abnormalities such as twisted toes, crooked beaks, badly sealed navels. Such birds are best destroyed right away. They seldom pay for keeping.

Killing Surplus or Poor Chicks

180. To kill a chick quickly and painlessly put the thumb of the right hand over the neck near the base of the skull and press against a sharp edged table or piece of board. This will instantly break the neck. This is far surer than striking the head against a wall and is cleaner. When done correctly

there is no bleeding and death is instantaneous. The poultry-man must not be too squeamish about killing second-grade chicks. Their retention is a definite source of danger to the others. The weakly bird is the first to pick up disease and will pass on the infection to the healthier stock.

Cleaning the Incubator

181. The incubator must be thoroughly cleaned and dis-infected between each hatch to prevent the spread of disease. Dismantle the interior fittings and wash them in a solution of disinfectant made up in accordance with the manufacturer's instructions. A very good and cheap disease-killing solution can be made by adding a double handful of washing soda to a bucket of hot water.

Fumigation

182. Fumigation with formaldehyde gas is now generally recommended before reloading the machine with eggs. This is a powerful disease-killing agent especially against certain bacterial infections. For the 150 size machine ½ oz. of perman-ganate of potash and 1 oz. of commercial formalin is required. Place the permanganate of potash crystals in a flat pan or dish in the incubator tray. Pour the formalin into the dish and immediately close the drawer. Let the gas remain active for three/four hours, and then air the machine well before re-use. To get the best results from this fumigation, cover up all air vents, have the temperature up to about 100° F. and have a certain amount of moisture in the machine. Prevent damage from the heat generated by removing the capsule and thermo-meter. When using this method be careful not to inhale the fumes as they have a strong action on the eyes and lungs.

183. On some commercial farms using the large forced draught machines the fumigation is carried out while the chicks are actually hatching. This is quite safe and does not harm the birds. It is important, however, to remember that once the chicks have been exposed to the formaldehyde gas they should not be subjected again to the same process. To produce the correct amount of gas for this method use 1¼ fluid ozs. of 40 per cent formalin and 0.6 oz. of permanganate of potash for each 100 cubic feet of incubator space.

Broody Hen Incubation

184. Hatching by means of the broody hen is a comparatively simple business. The two most important factors being:—

(a) a really broody hen

and

(b) a clean well-made coop.

To ensure that the bird selected is broody put her in the coop with a few spare eggs two or three days before the hatching eggs are introduced. If she sits "tight" and shows no inclination to leave the nest it is safe to remove the original eggs and replace with those to be hatched. Do this at night and go back an hour or so later to confirm that she has accepted the "sitting."

185. A clean vermin-free coop is essential if the hen is to remain in good condition during her period of sitting, so thoroughly disinfect the woodwork before use. Also add some insect powder to the hay or straw litter and rub a little on the hen under the wings, near the vent and round the head. The broody coop should measure about two feet square and should be approximately two feet high at the front sloping to 1 ft. 6 in. at the back. The front should be provided with slats of wood so spaced that the hen is confined. The centre slat should be removable to permit the broody to leave the coop for feeding, etc. Provide a good solid floor to prevent attacks by rats. For the same reason provide a piece of board for placing over the front of the coop at night. To allow a free current of fresh air several one inch holes should be bored near the top. This additional protection will keep out vermin during their most active time.

Number of Eggs Per Hen

186. It is usual to give each hen about twelve eggs during the colder months of the year and fifteen/sixteen when the weather is warm. Once a day—during the brooding period—the hen should be allowed to leave the nest for exercise, feeding, etc., for about twenty minutes. In very cold weather it is advisable to restrict the time the broody is away to not more than fifteen minutes, and during this period some poultry keepers cover the eggs with a piece of flannel to prevent chilling. When the chicks begin to hatch do not let the broody out but place food and water within her reach.

187.   It is best to leave the hen to herself while the chicks are actually hatching. The broken shells can be removed and any tidying up done when all the hatchable chicks are out of their shells.

188.   The questions of temperature and humidity do not arise with natural incubation. The hen will effectively look after these details. In very extreme weather (both hot or cold) however, the poultryman can do much to increase the comfort of the hen. In bad weather the coop should be placed in a sheltered position or better still it can be installed in an airy shed. In summer the coop should be slightly raised off the ground. This will allow a flow of air under the coop and will help to keep the interior temperature down. A sack placed to intercept the hot midday sun also makes conditions easier for the broody. It is little things such as these that indicate the good poultryman. He will always think of the comfort of his stock because he knows that a happy contented bird will give better results. Poultry cannot tolerate extremely hot weather unless they are given adequate protection, and to leave a broody hen in a small coop exposed to the full glare of the midday sun is asking for trouble. Death from heat prostration may speedily ensue with the attendant loss of the sitting of eggs.

CHAPTER VI

REARING

Effect of Low Temperatures

189. No matter how good the breeding system or the standard of management may be, if the chick rearing is not done well then the whole poultry venture will be a failure. Chicks are a strange mixture of self-reliance and dependance. They can, within a few hours of hatching, walk about steadily and eat and drink without tuition. But they have very little resistance to exposure to low temperatures for prolonged periods. It is this last fact that accounts for so much of the disappointment experienced by small poultry keepers who buy their chicks in markets.

Buying Chicks

190. It is a common occurrence to see boxes of chicks, with the lids removed exposed for several hours in some of the country markets. It is small wonder that the unfortunate youngsters die soon after being purchased. It cannot be too strongly emphasized that if chicks are bought they should be purchased direct from a breeder or hatchery. They may cost a few extra pence this way but there is compensation in the knowledge that the birds will stand a fairly reasonable chance of living. The birds will also be of the sex required. It is quite common to hear that domestic poultry keepers buying so-called pullets from a market find—weeks later—that 90 per cent of the chicks are cockerels. It is obviously false economy to buy cheaply if there is a risk of getting poor quality or incorrectly sexed chicks. Be sure—deal direct with a firm of repute. Often it costs no more, and there is the added guarantee that the seller has his reputation to consider.

Broody Hen Rearing

191. The small poultry keeper who is interested in rearing only ten or twelve pullets frequently makes use of a broody hen. In these circumstances much of the work and worry associated with artificial rearing disappears. The main trouble will

be to get a broody hen just at the time required, particularly early in the season. It is fatal to give a batch of chicks to a hen that does not really want to sit. She will refuse to brood them and may even kill them.

192.   If it is intended to place purchased chicks under a hen make sure well in advance that the bird is broody. She can be given a few eggs a week or so before the date that the chicks are expected. If she sits "tightly" on the eggs then all is well and the chicks can be introduced to her when they arrive. Do this preferably after dark as the hen will settle down more quickly when there is nothing to distract her attention. Put each chick in the coop separately and after they have been placed under the hen, remove the eggs; wait for a time to see that the chicks are well received. If the change is done quietly the broody will not usually realise what has happened.

Size of Run
193.   For natural rearing a run about four/five feet long, two feet wide, and about nine/ten inches high should be attached to the broody coop. The whole unit should be moved to fresh ground each day. When space is too limited to allow this the run can be equipped with a $\frac{1}{2}$ in. wire netting floor raised several inches off the ground. During the first fourteen/ twenty-one days of rearing the hen is usually restricted to the coop so that the youngsters can get warm quickly when they feel chilly. After this stage has been passed the small run can be replaced by a wire netting enclosure and the hen allowed to wander within its boundaries with the chicks.

Artificial Methods
194.   Rearing by the natural system is only a proposition where very small numbers are concerned, and the great majority of chicks are now reared by artificial methods. In the past there was much criticism of these methods but experience has proved that a good brooder or foster mother will turn out chicks every bit as good as those produced by the broody hen. As with incubation there are numerous rearing appliances on the market and a detailed account of the actual operation of the various models would be quite impossible here.

Size of Batch

195. It is therefore proposed to deal with the main principles involved, as a knowledge of these will help the poultryman to choose the type most suited to his own particular circumstances. In artificial rearing the actual size of the batch of chicks reared together has some influence on the results obtained. Rearing appliances are made to hold anything from 12 to 500 chicks and the larger units are suitable only on very big farms. Even there, there is now little enthusiasm for the 250/500 size batches, as although labour is reduced there is a far greater risk of losses as one diseased bird will often pass on the infection to the remainder of the batch. The twelve/fifty units on the other hand are very expensive to operate and present problems when large numbers are involved.

196. The ideal number of chicks to rear in one batch is about 75/100. With brooders of this size labour costs are comparatively low, disease is kept within reasonable limits, and what is more important is that it is possible for the attendant to keep each bird under observation. In larger units there is the tendency to miss such points as minor injuries or the odd "off-colour" chick. The neglect of these small factors frequently leads to more serious trouble. Young chicks have latent cannibalistic tendencies and a bird with a bleeding wound, if overlooked, may be the cause of an outbreak of cannibalism. Likewise the weakly chick is often diseased and may spread the trouble to the others before it is noticed.

197. Most large commercial farms have now adopted the 100 chick size unit, and the general opinion is that it is the best for all normal purposes.

198. There are three main types of artificial rearing namely:—

    (a)   The intensive system
    (b)   The extensive system
    (c)   The battery system

Intensive System

199. The intensive system is based on keeping the birds in special houses or brooders away from the soil until they are ready to dispense with heat.

200. The usual lay-out of an intensive brooder house consists of a number of brooding compartments each about 10 ft. x 9 ft. with a service passage down one side for convenient working. Inside each compartment is a hover heated by oil, electricity or water. The front of the house is boarded to a height of twelve inches from the ground, the rest of the structure consisting of glass shutters (in front of fixed wire netting) that can be removed or folded down to provide fresh air and direct sunlight for the chicks. After the first week these shutters should be open at all times except when violent winds or driving rain would blow in on the young stock. For the first few days the chicks are confined near the hover by means of a circle of wire netting, but as soon as they learn to find the heat they are given the full run of the compartment. Coddling must be avoided. It does not matter how cold the compartment is so long as the temperature under the hover is sufficient to warm the birds when they feel chilly. A thermometer reading of 90/95° F. taken two inches off the litter at a position mid-way between the source of heat and the edge of the canopy is satisfactory for the first seven days of rearing. There should be a gradual reduction in

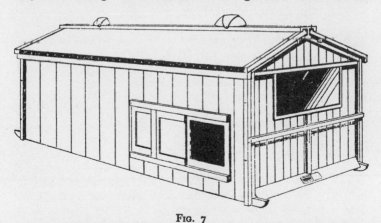

Fig. 7

A very efficient 100 chick size outdoor brooder suitable for rearing from day-old to weaning. The unit measures 6 ft. x 4 ft. and is equipped with sliding roofs to facilitate handling the brooder lamp, etc.
(Manufactured by Papworth Industries Ltd.)

temperature after this until the birds are no longer in need of heat at all—usually at five/six weeks.

Brooding Temperatures

201. There should be no fixed rules regarding hover temperatures, the behaviour of the chicks is the best guide. If they are too cold they will crowd near the source of heat and if too warm will move away from the hover canopy and in extreme cases will be found gasping for breath.

202. Both chilling and over-heating must be avoided. These two factors probably account for more losses than all the poultry diseases put together. The aim at all times should be to keep the youngsters comfortable. This does not mean keeping them in a stuffy atmosphere but providing sufficient warmth where it is needed—under the hover canopy.

203. When leaving the birds for the night it is a good plan to adjust the temperature so that the chicks arrange themselves evenly round the heater. If the nearest are three or four inches away from the lamp there will be a safety margin should the temperature fall greatly during the early hours of the morning. The chicks will be able to close up without any danger of crushing.

Litter

204. The floor of the intensive brooding compartments should be covered with litter to a depth of $2\frac{1}{2}/3$ inches and this should be removed as soon as it shows signs of becoming damp. The area under and near the hover will require replacement more often than the rest as it is here that the chicks will spend a good proportion of their time.

Overcrowding

205. The main thing to guard against with the intensive system is overcrowding. A compartment less than 10 ft. x 9 ft. will not be large enough for 100 chicks after they are four weeks old so do not economise by trying to run more chicks than the space available will permit. Overcrowding leads to many common rearing troubles. Feather plucking, toe picking and actual cannibalism may result. So may general unthriftiness and poor rate of growth.

Raised Brooders

206. There has been a growing tendency for some time to modify the normal intensive system by using 100 size brooders raised off the floor. These units are frequently equipped with wire floors and resemble the battery system. They have, however, none of the latter's disadvantages.

FIG. 8

A typical all-metal tier brooder. Each tier will accommodate 100 chicks to three/four weeks of age.
(Manufactured by Cope & Cope Ltd.).

207. Essentially these raised brooders consist of a heated brooding compartment and an unheated run for exercise. Food and water utensils are slung outside the run for easy filling and to prevent contamination by the birds' droppings. I have used these for many thousands of chicks and can definitely recommend them. They are easy to operate, take little labour and produce good quality chicks. When fitted with electric heating thermostatically controlled, many of the headaches associated with chick rearing disappear. I have

recently tried out a Calor gas unit with thermostatic heat control, and for poultrymen without electricity this method has much to recommend it. There is very little risk of fire and an ample reserve of heat even for the coldest weather. As the gas is supplied in portable cylinders it can be installed in any location. The thermostat ensures that gas consumption is kept to a minimum and at the same time maintains a safe temperature irrespective of outside weather conditions.

208. With these raised wire floored brooders it is important to remember that although they will accommodate 100 day-old chicks they are not large enough to run on this number until the birds are six/seven weeks old. It is necessary to divide the batch in two when the birds are about $3\frac{1}{2}$ weeks old.

Ventilation of Brooder House

209. A second point of importance—sometimes overlooked—is that the brooder house should be well ventilated. The small amount of space taken up by these brooders, especially when there are several tiers to each unit, results in housing many more chicks than would be the case if they were brooded on the floor. A good flow of air through the house is essential. The fitting of extractor cowls and properly baffled floor-level air intakes to change the air eight times an hour is the ideal system as this prevents draughts, but at the same time allows ample fresh air to the birds. (See chapter on housing).

Extensive System

210. The second method of brooding—known as the extensive system—allows the chicks to come in contact with the ground at a very early age. The system depends on the use of small outdoor brooders fitted with runs. Many breeders prefer this method to any other as they say it produces better stock birds. There is, however, considerable controversy on the matter. Contact with the earth at an early age may bring in its train certain diseases especially if the land has been used by poultry for a number of years. When it is possible to reserve a certain amount of fresh clean land each year for chick rearing the danger is not so great. There is much to be said on both sides. Certainly the modern outdoor brooder is efficient and will rear good sturdy chicks, and a large

number are in use on breeding farms. They are heavier on labour than is the case with the intensive system as greater distances have to be covered when feeding, watering, etc.

Outdoor Rearing in Cold Weather

211. The small outdoor brooder should be located in a reasonably protected spot especially when used during the very cold weather. Difficulty is found—in some models—in obtaining a high enough temperature for the first five days of rearing if the brooder is placed in an exposed position during bad weather. The location of the units is therefore of prime importance. For rearing during November to February it is advisable to choose a spot where the brooders are sheltered from cold winds. A small field protected by thick hedges on the north and east sides is admirable. Alternatively, an orchard will provide shelter both in winter and summer, and makes an ideal rearing ground.

212. As the birds have access to the ground there is less danger of overcrowding, as the youngsters use the actual brooder very little during the day-time after the first two or three weeks. Also, as the birds grow they can be given more room by extending the wire netting run.

Moving the Brooders

213. To avoid contaminated land it is usual to move the brooders and runs every two or three days. This regular moving is important as some of the poultry parasites responsible for heavy chick losses mature in the soil. Frequent moving has the effect of keeping such troubles under control. Success with outdoor brooders largely depends on keeping the ground free from these common poultry disease germs. Therefore, adult birds should never be permitted to range over the land ear-marked for the youngsters as most fully-grown fowls are carriers of these organisms although they themselves are not affected.

Size of Outdoor Brooder

214. The usual size for an extensive brooder to take 100 chicks is about 6 ft. x 4 ft. A unit of this size will accommodate the chicks until they are weaned from heat and is usually easy to move—quite an important factor in view of the frequency with which the unit is moved to clean land.

Feeding Trough Space

215. A point sometimes overlooked by beginners is that as the chicks grow they must be given additional feeding trough space especially if wet mash is fed. To obtain maximum growth it is essential that there should be no jostling for a place at the food trough. Unless there is room for all the birds the weakest will not get their fair share and will consequently not develop properly. Apart from the fact that the batch will look uneven there is the very real danger that the "poor doers" may have little resistance to disease and may be the cause of high mortality throughout the batch. One infected chick may be the start of a serious disease outbreak. The value of ample feeding space is therefore obvious.

The Battery System

216. The third method—the battery system—consists of rearing the chicks in special heated cages. The brooder is similar to the tier brooder except that the whole compartment is heated. It is really a large wire-floored hover with the food and water troughs attached outside. The general principle of operation is to reduce the heat of the compartment as the birds grow older. Frequently this is done by moving the chicks down to the next lower tier or to other units operated at a lower temperature. The great disadvantage of this system is that it tends to create "soft" birds as they do not get the stimulation of contact with cold air. From the view-point of the poultryman who wants birds for future breeding operations the system is bad. Battery reared birds are rather like hot house plants—they do not stand up well to the more rigorous conditions on the average farm. For birds that are to be killed at sixteen weeks, however, this does not matter and the low running costs involved make the system worth while in such circumstances.

Floor Area per Bird

217. One of the most frequent complaints made by battery operators is that of cannibalism. In the necessarily restricted environment the risk of feather pulling, toe picking, etc., is always present. It is accentuated to an alarming degree should there be over-crowding. The number of chicks to keep in

one compartment depends on the size of the actual unit but the following figures are given as a guide:—

12 square inches per chick up to 2 weeks

20/24 square inches per chick from 2 to 4 weeks

40/50 square inches per chick from 4 to 6 weeks

It is false economy to give the chicks less space than this as outbreaks of cannibalism will more than offset any gains on the reduced capital expenditure involved.

218. To summarize the question of brooding it may be said that each system has its advantages and disadvantages, and the poultryman must decide for himself which is best for the purpose he has in mind.

The Growing Period

219. Chicks can be weaned from heat at any time from five/six weeks onwards according to the type of "follow-on" equipment used and the weather prevailing. Normally most farms wean their chicks at seven/eight weeks of age and then house them in small portable houses known as night arks. The standard night ark is approximately six feet long by three feet wide and has a slatted floor. This type of housing is extremely good, and has the great advantage of economy as it is a useful all-purpose house. It can accommodate young growing stock during the spring and summer and for the rest of the year can be used to hold small batches of adults providing a suitable nest box is placed inside.

Weaning from Heat

220. The general procedure adopted when weaning the chicks from heat is to reduce the temperature of the hover or foster-mother gradually until no heat is supplied at all during the day and only a little on very cold nights. It is useless to give detailed suggestions regarding temperatures for each successive week. Be guided by the birds. As they begin to get their feathers they will tend to get further away from the brooder lamp if they are too hot. Towards the end of the brooding period they will space themselves comfortably in the brooder with the minimum of heat. After about four/five weeks there is little danger of chilling but there is the possibility that if insufficient heat is supplied at night the

stock may huddle into a corner and heavy losses can result from smothering. The strongest birds will force themselves into the corner of the brooder and may then be smothered by the weight of the others trying to get as close as possible.

221. The same trouble may occur when putting the growers into night arks. To prevent such losses some poultrymen line the slatted floor with straw or a clean sack. This reduces the flow of air through the ark, and helps to maintain a comfortable temperature for the first week or so. When weaning birds in severe weather it helps considerably if a hurricane lantern is suspended in the ark. This not only keeps up the temperature but also draws the birds away from the corners thus preventing losses through huddling.

Capacity of Night Arks

222. A 6 ft. x 3 ft. night ark will hold up to sixty chicks at weaning time. It should be remembered, however, that the

FIG. 9

Slatted floor night ark complete with handles for easy moving and alternative solid wood and wire netting doors. The solid door is closed at night during cold weather or when the growing birds have just been moved from the brooders, and the wire door later on in the season to increase the ventilation during very hot weather.
(Manufactured by Tom M. Scotney Ltd.).

youngsters grow quickly at this stage and that not more than forty-five should be housed in the unit after they are three months old. From 4½ months to maturity it is advisable to reduce the number to twenty-five/thirty—particularly during the warmer weather.

Protection for Growers

223. For the first two or three weeks after weaning some form of protection from the wind should be given. The youngsters can tolerate quite low temperatures without taking any harm, but they will not make good growth if subjected to the buffeting of strong winds.

224. A wattle hurdle placed near the ark to intercept the prevailing wind is very effective in giving shelter to the stock. a timber frame covered with sacking will also do the same job.

Space Between Arks

225. When several arks are in use at one time in the same field, allow plenty of space between them—ten or twelve yards is about the minimum distance. If placed nearer than this there is a chance that older batches will bully the younger ones and prevent them from getting their fair share of food, etc. Another point is that the birds often tend to pack into one ark at night and this is accentuated if the houses are placed close together. In order to accustom each batch to roost in its own ark it is usual to enclose the unit with a wire netting run for a few days. This prevents the new occupants from wandering, and incidentally also helps to keep off the bigger birds until the youngsters have had time to settle down.

226. An aid to good even growth is the provision of ample food and water utensils. With several age groups of growers in one field or enclosure the younger birds will stand little chance if there is insufficient trough space. They will be pushed away until the older birds have had their fill. Each ark should have its own food and water containers, and when feeding start by filling the troughs of the oldest batch first. If the young ones are fed first the others are bound to rush to join in.

Food Requirements During Rearing

227. Details concerning the amount of food required to rear chicks to maturity will be found in the chapter dealing

with feeding, and it cannot be too strongly emphasized that it is unwise to attempt to rear more birds than there is food for. The temptation is strong, but it is far better to keep the numbers down so that each gets a good start in life. Poorly nourished stock makes slow growth, and when mature will usually suffer from its inadequate nutritional background. Such adults are an easy prey to disease and are not a sound proposition. A few birds well fed and correctly managed can show a larger profit than double the number on a poor diet.

CHAPTER VII

MANAGEMENT

228. The day-to-day routine for running a poultry flock is very much an individual affair as each unit and farm has its own particular system. What applies on one does not necessarily apply to all. There is, however, a certain standard of efficiency that must be maintained if the venture is to be a success.

Importance of Observation

229. Constant observation of the stock is supremely important, and the daily work should be so organised that the poultryman has time to spend a few minutes with each group of birds. This regular study will more than repay the time taken. Practically all the major troubles occasionally experienced on any farm start in a small way, and if the attendant uses his eyes he can often prevent heavy losses by adopting suitable precautionary measures.

230. For example, most outbreaks of cannibalism start by one bird plucking a few feathers from another. If this state of affairs is neglected, sooner or later blood will be drawn and the whole flock will become involved—probably with fatal results. Likewise, if the birds show little enthusiasm for their food one morning, this is often a sign that something is wrong. Good management demands that any such departures from the normal should be investigated right away.

231. If symptoms of unusual behaviour are observed, find out what is causing the variation. Do not be afraid to seek advice from others if the reason cannot be located. The poultryman can always call on the services of the local Poultry Advisory Officer if he is in difficulty, or if the case is not urgent can consult one of the specialist poultry papers.

Keep the Stock Comfortable

232. Good management is mainly a question of doing everything possible to ensure that the birds are kept contented and comfortable. The ability to do this is acquired

gradually. As each year passes the poultryman, if he is observant, learns a little more about the behaviour and needs of his flock with the result that eventually trouble can often be anticipated before it starts.

Annual Moult

233. Particular care should be exercised when the birds are going through the annual moult, as this is a critical time. There is a good deal of muddled thinking about the management of poultry during this period. As the birds are no longer producing eggs many imagine that they need less food or food of a poorer quality than usual. Although the birds no longer require the nourishment normally absorbed by the eggs, they have a particular need of protein-rich nutrients for the growth of the new feathers. It is wrong therefore to change the feeding during the moult. Keep the stock on a good diet and it will be back in production much quicker and in better condition than if compelled to grow new feathers on a badly balanced ration.

234. Normally birds moult once a year, the first moult occurring in the late summer or early autumn of the year following that in which they were hatched. It frequently happens, however, that stock hatched early in the season (January—February) will go into a moult in the autumn of the same year. The reason for this is that as the days shorten so the birds have less opportunity of supplementing their ration with tit-bits gleaned from the fields, etc. This reduction of food intake when coupled with poor body condition places too much strain on the birds.

235. The way to avoid premature moulting with early hatched stock is to ensure that the birds are kept in good condition. Generous feeding during the late spring and summer while they are laying, plus an extra evening feed as the days draw in will often have the desired result. It is not easy these days when food is dear to be over generous with the rations, but unless the early hatched stock does start the autumn in really plump condition a certain amount of moulting must be expected. In the case of the poultryman who wants to use the pullets for breeding this rest from laying is not unwelcome. The birds—after a rest—will come back into production just at the time when the eggs are required for

incubation. In addition, the egg size is usually improved after the moult and this means that most of the eggs produced are suitable for hatching purposes.

236. The commercial egg farmer views the matter from quite a different angle. He wants winter eggs because they make a better price. The management of a flock of early hatched pullets will therefore vary according to the purpose for which it is kept.

237. In most flocks odd birds will be found which seem to be moulting the whole time. Such birds should be culled as they produce very few eggs. They can be detected by their smart appearance. When the bulk of the layers look rather worn and ragged with broken feathers the continuous moulter will have new plumage. Another bird to cull is the female that moults very early in the season (June—July). These are almost invariably poor layers and will probably not come back into production until the rest of the flock.

238. The actual time taken by the birds to equip themselves with a new coat of feathers varies considerably. It is mainly influenced by the speed with which the old feathers were shed. The quick moulter will therefore be back in the nest box doing her job of laying much sooner than the bird that drops a few feathers at a time. Other things being equal the best birds to retain are those that moult late in the season (September—October) and that spend the minimum time in the process.

Broodiness

239. Another factor calling for some degree of skilled management is the control of broodiness. All the heavy breeds exhibit this desire to "sit" (the light breeds such as the Leghorns, Anconas, Minorcas, etc. seldom go broody). It is an entirely natural function. As the weather becomes warmer in spring—the natural hatching season—a proportion of the layers will be found on the nests brooding a batch of eggs. Unless steps are taken immediately to break this desire the female concerned will cease egg production and probably will not start laying again for about six weeks.

240. Here again observation plays a large part in tackling the problem. Any birds remaining on the nest at feeding time and that protest vigorously at being removed should be classed

as broodies. If dealt with right away the desire to sit can be broken in a few days and egg production will suffer very little. There are several ways of curing a broody hen. One which is generally satisfactory is to put the bird into a special coop equipped with a wooden slatted or wire netting floor. This prevents her from sitting comfortably and after a few days of this she will be back to normal. During this period of detention the hen must have plenty of fresh water and ordinary food. It is a great mistake to neglect the broody hens as if deprived of their full diet they may lose body condition and go out of production altogether.

241.   Another way of correcting the brooding instinct is to put any hens showing the symptoms into a pen with a vigorous cockerel. Do not provide nest boxes or floor litter. This will usually prove effective in a very short time.

242.   Broodiness is an inherited characteristic and when selecting birds for the breeding pen it is desirable not to include those that have shown an excessive desire to go broody. As a means of checking on this point make it part of the routine to place a red legband on any bird put into the broody breaking coop. At the end of the season the females with several legbands can be scrapped as they have obviously got this undesirable factor in their genetical make-up and will most probably pass it on to their offspring.

Hot Weather

243.   Good management can also do much to promote healthy stock. The chapter on hygiene outlines the salient features in providing a clean environment, but in addition to this there are many small things that the poultryman can do to assist his birds. During warm weather, for example, particular care should be taken to keep parasites under control. Fleas, lice, and red mite multiply with extreme rapidity when the weather is hot and unless these pests are fought vigorously they will quickly reduce the condition of the stock to such an extent that its resistance to disease may be weakened.

244.   Dusting the birds with a D.D.T. powder should be a regular part of the routine during the summer. A pinch of the powder rubbed in under the wings, on the abdomen and round the head and neck will keep the stock comfortable. Some of the

(**A**)   White Wyandotte Female

(**B**)   White Wyandotte Male

(**C**)   Silver Sebright Male

(**D**)   White Polish Female

(**E**)   Silver Spangled Hamburg Female

(**F**)   Buff Plymouth Rock Female

PLATE VII

(**A**) Mammoth Bronze Turkey (Male) in an intensive unit

(**B**) A flock of Aylesburys on a large du breeding farm

(**C**) While not essential for successful breeding both ducks and geese appreciate the luxury of swimming water. In the background can be seen the simple shed used to house the flock

(**D**) Geese are excellent foragers and w get a large part of their keep if giv plenty of range. Young fruit tre should be protected as illustrated wire netting to prevent damage

PLATE VIII

same compound sprinkled in the nest boxes and on the litter will likewise reduce infestation to a minimum.

245. The summer is really the most difficult time for the poultry-keeper. Every year during hot spells a comparatively large number of fowls die from heat prostration. To prevent this ensure that the houses are well ventilated and that the stock has ample shade in the runs. Shade should also be provided for the water container as sun-heated water is both unpalatable and bad for the flock. Special care should be taken to keep the food troughs clean—especially if wet mash is fed—as any food residue will sour in the course of a day or so.

Dosing the Stock

246. Regular dosing with medicines, etc., in the drinking water is recommended by some, but in my own opinion this is an unwise policy. The stock, if given a good clean environment and adequate nutrition does not need "doping". In certain circumstances, such as the outbreak of disease, the addition of a suitable hypochlorite disinfectant in the water may be of some value, but it should not be made a permanent feature of the management routine.

Soft Shelled Eggs

247. A query frequently raised is how to prevent soft-shelled eggs or shell-less eggs. In most cases the production of eggs with a poor quality shell is due to some deficiency in the diet. There should be, at all times, a supply of calcium available to the birds. This can be in the form of shell or limestone grit. This by itself, however, is not sufficient as the birds cannot make use of this material for egg-shell production unless there is also sufficient vitamin D in the diet. Therefore during the winter months—and in the case of intensively kept birds—cod liver oil at the rate of 1 per cent should be added to the mash.

248. Even this will not always prevent soft-shelled eggs. Some birds will not produce a normal egg whatever their diet, and such offenders should be culled and sent to the table. The proportion involved, however, is small and when the bulk of the flock is concerned the fault is in the diet. When young pullets first come into production they frequently lay shell-less or badly shelled eggs. This is quite normal and will

4

correct itself as soon as the birds settle down to regular laying.

Egg Eating

249. The vice of egg eating is another common trouble and unfortunately it is very difficult to cure. It is best tackled on the basis of providing conditions that do not favour its development. The nests should be placed in the darkest part of the house, and plenty of nest space should be provided. The regular collection of eggs also helps. Egg eating often starts because an egg is broken in the nest and is sampled by one of the birds. Once a chicken has acquired the taste for eggs she is best removed from the pen as she will usually continue to give trouble. The provision of ample nest box space will do much to prevent accidental breakage, but if in spite of this, egg eating does start, then some reduction of the vice may result if the nests are placed in almost total darkness. A piece of sacking tacked in position in front of the nests with slits to permit the entry of the layers has been found effective on some farms. Eggs filled with mustard, etc., can be tried although their value is much less than generally imagined. Removing the tip of birds' beaks is another suggested remedy. This—at the best—provides only a temporary alleviation of the vice as the debeaking has to be done every two/three weeks to be effective.

250. Careful observation will show those birds responsible and their removal plus the darkening of the nest boxes is really the best method of treatment.

Egg Binding

251. Occasionally a case of egg-binding will occur. This is usually caused by the presence of a very large egg in the oviduct which the bird cannot expel. The bird in such cases will be noticed straining hard to lay and looking very distressed. She may be helped by holding her over a container of boiling water and by smearing the vent with olive oil. If this does not result in the egg being laid within two or three hours then an endeavour should be made to remove the egg. Gently insert a finger—previously coated with vaseline—into the vent and try to work the egg out. In extreme cases it may be necessary to break the egg inside the bird. When this is done it is essential to ensure that every particle of the broken egg is removed or death from peritonitis may result.

Prolapsus

252. Another condition frequently arising, particularly with pullets in heavy production, is the eversion of the oviduct—usually referred to as prolapsus. A part of the oviduct protrudes from the vent and unless this is attented to immediately the other birds will start pecking at the mass with fatal results to the victim. Treatment, if prompt, may be effective. The exposed organs should be washed with warm water to which has been added a small quantity of disinfectant. They should then be gently returned but before handling the protruding mass make sure that the hands are properly clean. When replaced the vent should be syringed with a solution of cold strong tea and the bird put into a separate pen for a few days and fed on a light diet.

253. Any birds successfully treated should be noted and if the condition recurs it is best to remove the bird entirely from the flock as it is obvious that the muscles are not strong enough to support this part of the intestines during heavy egg production periods. The greatest danger from prolapsus is that an unnoticed case may give rise to an outbreak of cannibalism in the pen.

Crop Binding

254. A few cases of crop binding or sour crop will occur in almost every poultry unit. The symptoms of this trouble are an enlarged crop and mopey condition. Treatment consists of administering a teaspoonful of olive oil and then massaging the impacted mass. Some authorities also recommend removing the crop contents by surgical means but unless the bird is of special value this is not worth while as it is a tedious business and unless skilfully done frequently leads to death.

255. The real cause of crop binding is usually poor general condition of the stock, as ordinary healthy birds will not suffer from this trouble even when ranging over long coarse grass. If, therefore, a high proportion of the flock is affected it is advisable to send a specimen bird to a laboratory for a detailed post-mortem examination.

Wounds and Cuts

256. Wounds and cuts should always receive prompt treatment, as with a little trouble these will heal without much bother. If neglected, however, germs gain entry into the

tissues and give rise to complications—possibly with the loss
of the bird. Small cuts are most easily treated on the spot with
an application of tincture of iodine. Larger wounds should be
thoroughly washed in a warm weak solution of disinfectant
and then dusted with iodoform or boracic acid powder.

Bumble Foot

257.   Bumblefoot is a common form of injury among poultry.
This is primarily caused by a cut or bruise on the pad underneath the foot into which germ organisms have penetrated.
A swelling and tenderness results which makes walking
difficult. The swelling should be cut with a clean knife and the
accumulated pus pressed out. The cavity left should be
dusted as suggested for wounds and the bird isolated for a
few days.

Scaly Leg

258.   Scaly leg is another condition affecting poultry.
It arises through the activities of a small mite which burrows
under the scales of the leg. The condition can be recognised
by an enlargement of the legs and the raising of the scales
As it is contagious any bird affected should be treated at once.
The legs should be brushed with a solution of paraffin and
linseed oil in equal parts. A stiff nail brush is the best thing to
use but be careful not to get the solution on the bird's skin as
severe irritation will be set up.

CHAPTER VIII

DUCKS, GEESE, TURKEYS, BANTAMS

259. In a book of this size it is impossible to cover adequately all the details of management connected with the four above species of poultry. Little more than a brief outline can be given. It can, however, be assumed that the successful running of any poultry flock follows very similar lines. The same basic principles apply to the keeping and breeding of ducks, geese, turkey and bantams as with ordinary fowls. There are, of course, certain differences and as far as possible these are indicated as they arise.

DUCKS

260. In the past there was considerable prejudice against the duck egg due to its somewhat peculiar flavour. The rather fishy taste was probably caused by the fact that most of the ducks were kept on general farms and were encouraged to get the bulk of their food from the local ponds and ditches.

261. Nowadays the eggs produced by a well managed flock taste very similar to the average hen's egg. In actual practice there is very little variation between the methods of feeding and managing the two species of poultry. Contrary to general belief there is no necessity for ducks to have access to water except for drinking purposes, and any domestic poultry keeper can run a small flock in his garden. In fact from his point of view the duck is a better proposition than the hen. The average well bred duck will produce more eggs and bigger eggs, requires a less elaborate house, and will make good use of all the waste greenfood from the kitchen garden. There is the slight disadvantage that ducks require more food than hens—(about 25 per cent more)—but on a small scale of operations and with household scraps this is not so important.

Breeds

262. If it is intended to keep ducks for egg production the best breed is undoubtedly the Khaki Campbell. This is a hardy and prolific layer and flock averages of 200/250 eggs per

bird a year are frequent. The White Campbell and the White Runner are also good egg producers but are not so prolific as the Khaki Campbell. The most popular table breed in this country is the Aylesbury. When properly fed this breed should be ready for eating when nine/ten weeks old. The youngsters at that age carry a good quantity of white flesh, and needless to say are in great demand when the new peas are in season. Another suitable breed for meat production is the Pekin although it does not quite equal the Aylesbury. There are also some very fine ornamental varieties and where there is plenty of space and no imperative need for eggs or flesh their breeding makes a pleasant hobby.

Housing

263.   The housing of ducks is a comparatively simple matter. The main requirements are good ventilation and a nest box capacity commensurate with the number of layers kept. Ducks lay first thing in the morning and the usual procedure is to keep them shut in until they have laid. They are therefore ideal for the late riser. Many duck keepers open their houses about 9-9.30 a.m. The necessity for ample nest box accommodation is obvious as the laying period is concentrated into a matter of two or three hours and not throughout the day as with chickens.

264.   Actually in the case of a domestic flock there is not the same necessity to keep the birds shut in as they will probably not have a great deal of land over which to roam. When the birds have access to comparatively free range, however, failure to wait until laying is finished might well mean a considerable loss of eggs from "laying away" in the hedgerows, etc.

265.   Any airy shed will serve for housing. An allowance of four square feet per bird is desirable, and one nest box is needed for each three layers. These should be placed at floor level and not raised up as for chickens. Ducks do not need coddling, and a shed with a wire netting front will prove ideal provided there is some provision to prevent wind and rain driving in on the birds. The floor should be well littered with shavings, peat moss, or straw. No perches are needed. Ducks love to range in search of tit-bits so make the run as large as possible. In a small pen—during bad weather—they

will soon reduce the grass to a quagmire, much to their delight and the poultryman's inconvenience.

Feeding
266. Feeding can be on the same lines as for chickens, except that the mash should be fed in a moist state. The system of a morning feed of wet mash followed by an afternoon ration of grain is commonly followed on commercial duck farms. The small duck keeper can use either a ready prepared layers' mash or can make use of a balancer to which has been added household scraps as suggested for chickens in the chapter on feeding.

Breeding
267. Good breeding results can be obtained even though no swimming water is available. In fact many commercial duck farms have now ceased to provide pools for their stock, though if a small pool is provided the birds will certainly appreciate the luxury. It is advisable if contemplating the construction of a pool to bear in mind that provision should be made for easy draining so that the water can be changed frequently.
268. For breeding purposes it is usual to mate one male to about six females. With the egg production breeds it may be possible to increase the number of females but in the case of the Aylesbury six will be sufficient for one male if good fertility is wanted.

Hatching
269. Incubation of the eggs—this extends over twenty-eight days—is normally done in machines or on a small scale by broody hens, ten eggs being the number given to each broody. When using artificial incubation methods a good deal of moisture is required, and the normal practice is to sprinkle the eggs daily with warm water. However, as advised in Chapter V, be guided by the instructions issued by the makers of the machine.

Rearing
270. Ducklings can be reared with the same equipment as for chicks except that a solid floor brooder is needed. The use of wire floors has not, up to now, proved generally satis-

factory. Floor space can be estimated on the basis of allowing approximately ½ square foot per duckling from day-old to seven days increasing gradually until the youngsters have about three square feet at eight weeks.

271. A hover temperature of 85°F. to 90°F. for the first week, reducing slowly until at the end of the fourth week the brooder lamp is turned out, will be suitable under normal weather conditions.

272. Feeding the youngsters on wet mash calls for a little more attention than the dry mash chick system. For the first seven days the ducklings should have five small feeds a day giving only as much as they will clear up in twenty/thirty minutes. The number of feeds can be reduced until at weaning time they are having three meals daily.

Management

273. Ducks do best if not disturbed. The quieter they are managed the better. Sudden movements when in the pen or too much noise when feeding should be avoided. Further, do not let dogs or cats chase the flock. The duck exhibits far more intelligence than the hen, and if properly managed will prove easy to handle. For example, a flock can be led from its sleeping quarters to a paddock for the day and will return in the evening to sleep without any bother or trouble. High wire netting is not necessary for enclosing the duck pen, and a three foot barrier is usually quite sufficient to keep the stock under control.

GEESE

274. To make a success of goose keeping it is essential to have plenty of land available. Geese are natural foragers with prodigious appetites. Unless they have freedom to wander and are thereby able to pick up a large proportion of their food they will not prove an economic proposition. Rough pasture can be grazed by geese in much the same way as by cattle. There is in fact one well-known farmer who started his farming venture by using flocks of geese to break up some rough land as he could not, at that time, afford to buy bullocks. They are excellent for breaking in a rough piece of land in preparation for a laid-out garden. They will get a living where other species of poultry would starve, but if

land is scarce and they have to be provided with all their food they will probably not show a profit at killing time.

275. There is little doubt that the best place for a flock of geese is the general farm. Here, after the initial rearing period, they will make good growth on two small grain feeds a day provided they have a good area over which to roam. During the harvest period they will need no feeding at all if they are let out on to the stubbles. To get maximum weight at Christmas they should be given two feeds a day of a suitable fattening diet from October onwards. This can be bulked out by the use of cooked mashed potatoes up to 50 per cent of the total weight of the ration. A pre-war mash frequently used was as follows:—

> 2 parts Ground Wheat
>
> 2 parts Maize Meal
>
> 2 parts Barley Meal
>
> 1 part Ground Oats
>
> ½ part Dried Skimmed Milk

276. Housing can be extremely simple. Any shed affording protection from bad weather and natural enemies such as the fox, will be suitable. On many farms no special provision is made and the birds take shelter for the night in a cartshed or similar structure. This, however, is not recommended as the birds will foul the implements.

Hatching

277. Hatching is usually done under broody hens. Young goslings are hardy and need very little protection. If reared artificially, heat need be supplied for only two weeks—less in the warm months of the year. Feeding during the first eight weeks can be on the lines suggested for chickens. There is no point in having a large variety of mashes for each type of poultry. A good standard chick mash or home-made substitute will prove suitable for practically any young birds.

Breeds

278. There are several varieties of geese—some growing to twenty-five/thirty lbs. The more popular size bird should weigh about twelve lbs. when ready for killing at Christmas.

4*

The Roman variety is a favourite, so is the Chinese. Both these are of medium size and are more in keeping with modern taste than the more heavily built Toulouse or Embden breeds.

Breeding

279. When making up the breeding pens allow for a ratio of one male to four or five females. A good female can continue to be used for breeding until she is seven or eight years old, but males should not be used after five or six years. Both sexes will live very much longer but after these ages will not give such good results.

TURKEYS

Housing

280. Many poultry keepers regard turkeys as the most difficult of all birds to rear. Their experience over many seasons has convinced them that the young poult's main aim in life is to die, usually at the stage when they have involved their owners in the expenditure of a great deal of money, time and trouble. This unfortunate state of affairs has arisen mainly because of lack of knowledge regarding young turkeys' most deadly enemy—the disease known as Blackhead. This scourge has been responsible for the loss of millions of pounds during the past twenty years and still presents a major problem to the man who wants to make turkey farming a worth while proposition.

281. There are a number of proprietary medicines on the market that will help the turkey keeper to combat this disease, and under certain circumstances their use will save heavy losses. The dosing of stock is, however, not the answer to any of the troubles affecting poultry.

282. An appreciation of the habits of the Blackhead parasite, and a system of management that gives it little chance to attack the flock will prove more efficient and cheaper in the long run.

283. Essentially, the disease is spread by a microscopic parasite that is passed out of the body of infected birds in the droppings. The other poults come in contact with the organism and as a result become infected. Thus the vicious circle goes on. Under certain conditions the parasite can

remain alive in the ground for comparatively long periods
and will give rise to an outbreak of the disease in subsequent
years. It is this that accounts for the fact that often a farm
will have a successful season or two when first taking up
turkeys. After a year or so, however, losses occur and from
then onwards each year's rearing becomes more difficult. An
additional complicating factor is that chickens frequently
harbour the Blackhead parasite without showing any of the
symptoms. For this reason it is most undesirable to attempt
the rearing of turkeys and fowls on the same farm unless
they can be strictly segregated from each other.

284. The easiest way to overcome the problem is to adopt
an intensive system of turkey rearing. A number of large
turkey farms have adopted such methods with great success.
During 1948, using intensive methods, the writer was able to
rear a flock of turkeys to maturity without a single death
from Blackhead, in spite of the fact that there were also
chickens on the same farm.

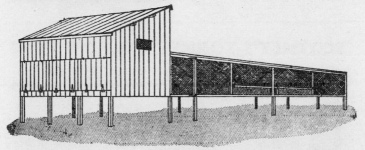

Fig. 10

The Animal Health Trust intensive turkey unit. Size 12 ft. wide by
20 ft. long. This provides accommodation for fifty growing turkeys
or twenty-five adults. The floor throughout is of wooden slats placed
1¼ inches apart.
(Manufactured by Tom M. Scotney Ltd.).

285. The unit used—illustrated in Fig. 10—was developed by
the Animal Health Trust and something on similar, if less
ambitious, lines could be made by any handyman. The
essential point of the unit is the use of slatted floors throughout.
The turkey droppings fall through the slats and thus the birds
have very little chance of pecking at infected material. They

have no contact at all with the soil and do not therefore pick up any infection that may be there from a previous year. Other types of intensive units are also in use commercially— some of them using strong wire netting or woven wire floors in place of wooden slats. The only objection to wire netting is the tendency for the stock to have foot trouble especially among the heavier breeds.

286. Even apart from the problem of disease, the small poultry keeper would be well advised to keep to intensive methods. In this way more birds can be kept on the land—the Animal Health Trust unit, for example, measures only 12 ft. x 20 ft. yet will accommodate twenty-five/thirty birds up to the killing stage. To run a similar number of turkeys on a pen basis would require at least ten to fifteen times this area ot land, and would possibly involve severe losses if the same plot were used year after year.

Feeding

287. The intensive system calls for careful attention to feeding methods. It used to be considered that turkeys needed large quantities of fresh green food when reared intensively. This is not the case, however, when using a properly balanced turkey mash, and there is no need to spend large sums on providing fresh greenstuff although the birds will relish a small quantity when available. A good proportion (up to 40 per cent) of cooked potatoes can be incorporated in the mash during the fattening period.

Incubation and Rearing

288. Both incubation and rearing can be carried on in much the same way as with other poultry. The use of broody hens is still popular with many small turkey breeders. This has obvious disadvantages from the viewpoint of disease, but if plenty of really clean land is available it can be quite successful. Artificial incubation (a twenty-eight day period) should be carried out on lines similar to those for ducks.

289. In comparison with chicks, slightly lower temperatures are required in the brooder and a reading of 85°F. for the first week reducing gradually till the poults are without heat at five to six weeks is sufficient. Later in the season the lamps can be dispensed with after four weeks.

290. Young turkey poults are not quite so self-reliant as

chicks and some difficulty may be experienced in getting them to eat. The first few feeds should be spread on a piece of board. The youngsters can be encouraged to investigate the mash by tapping gently on the board with the finger. Usually a little perseverence at this stage will soon get them started.

Breeds

291. There is not a great choice in the breeds of turkeys. The most popular is probably the Mammoth Bronze. This is rather a heavy bird and will produce males weighing up to 30 lbs.—the females grading out at 14-18 lbs. when ready for killing. A smaller variety—also very popular—is the Black Norfolk, and is probably a better proposition for the average oven.

Breeding

292. In the breeding pen one male will be sufficient to fertilise the eggs from eight/ten females. Old males usually become too heavy for use as stock birds and it is desirable to replace the stag each year. The females can be used for four or five seasons. There is a tendency for them to start laying later each year, so a certain proportion of young birds should be added to the flock annually to secure some eggs reasonably early in the season.

293. Another method of securing early eggs is to provide artificial lights in the pen during the darker months at the beginning of the year. These stimulate the birds' ovaries and egg production will start sooner. However, in view of the modern demand for small-sized turkeys it is doubtful whether very early hatching is desirable as most poultrymen rear their birds for the Christmas market.

BANTAMS

294. The possession of a flock of bantams is probably the most intriguing aspect of poultry keeping. These miniatures make a great appeal to those people who have only a very limited space available for their hobby. From a commercial point of view bantams are of little value but as a hobby they can give endless pleasure and have the great advantage that a breeding pen takes up only a small corner of a surburban

garden. There is also the advantage that certain breeds are prolific layers of medium-sized eggs and require very much less food than their larger sisters.

295. It is possible to keep three or four bantams on the same amount of food as two ordinary pullets would need. And if the egg production is in the region of 80 per cent of that of the larger birds the gain in eggs is obvious. Not all the bantams, however, are good egg producers but some strains of miniature Rhode Island Red and Light Sussex are excellent.

296. Most bantam enthusiasts are keen breeders and the man or woman who wants to take up this most interesting hobby should join their local poultry fanciers' club. Here they will get some first hand information regarding the various breeds and will find a helping hand to start them on their way to the show bench.

Management

297. The general management of a bantam flock is very similar to that of normal poultry. They require the same type of food and housing although of course they eat less and need a smaller area for their accommodation. For example a house suitable for six birds need measure no more than 4 ft. long by 3 ft. wide with a height of $2\frac{1}{2}/3$ ft. A run 10 ft. long by 4 ft. wide and 5 ft. high would provide ample room for outdoor exercise, etc. To get the best results it is advisable to provide the stock with shelter from strong winds. This can be achieved either by locating the pen in a sheltered part of the garden or by boarding up the run for about eighteen inches from the ground. Hessian screens will also serve to intercept the prevailing winds.

298. With some bantam breeds difficulty may be experienced in getting hens to brood the eggs. The Silkie Bantam hen, however, has a wonderful reputation as a mother and some bantam breeders always keep a few of this variety to act as the incubators and foster mothers to the flock.

299. The same procedure for managing the broody hens is followed as with ordinary poultry except that the chicks normally hatch out a little earlier—the usual incubating period being nineteen/twenty days.

300. Although bantams are not generally so hardy as the larger varieties of poultry and need a less exposed position

it is fatal to coddle the stock. A tendency towards insufficient ventilation in the house will frequently bring about an outbreak of colds. If this does happen, isolate the infected birds to prevent the trouble spreading and make sure that the remainder of the flock has ample fresh air passing through the roosting compartment.

301.   The birds with colds should have their nostrils bathed with warm water containing a few crystals of permanganate of potash to keep the passage clear, and should be fed on a diet containing a liberal quantity of vitamin A (Plenty of fresh green food and the addition of 1 per cent veterinary cod liver oil will provide this protective vitamin).

302.   Apart from the varieties kept for egg production there are a considerable number of fancy breeds for the prospective bantam breeder to choose from as most of the larger breeds have their miniature counterparts. Perhaps the most interesting group of all is the Old English Game. It has a wonderful fascination partly because of the difficulty in producing a first-class show bird and partly on account of the real beauty of some of the males.

CHAPTER IX

HYGIENE AND SANITATION ON THE POULTRY FARM

By Dr. R. F. GORDON, M.R.C.V.S.

303. It is not proposed in this chapter to describe the cause, symptoms, treatment or control of the very numerous diseases which may affect poultry. A subject of this type dealt with adequately would form a text book in itself, in fact such text books do exist and if the reader is disposed to dip more deeply into the subject of poultry pathology, he should refer to the many works published on this subject. (Two of the cheaper editions are listed at the end of this chapter.)

304. In the main few of the infectious diseases of poultry give rise to symptoms sufficiently characteristic to be recognised by the layman and a mere list of these conditions would only lead to further confusion. It should be remembered that facilities do exist for the post-mortem examination of dead carcases by qualified veterinary pathologists at a number of laboratories. When an owner is faced with sick or dying birds he will be well advised to consult his county poultry advisory officer or Domestic Poultry Keepers' Council organiser who can advise him as to the nearest laboratory where this work is undertaken and to which typical and infected carcases should be sent. In sending such specimens do remember to enclose a concise history giving the details of the total number of birds kept, the number which are affected or which have died, period of time over which the disease has occurred, and the salient clinical symptoms. Better still, list these details in that order and leave out the irrelevant material which only serves to confuse the busy pathologist.

305. As a result of the rapid expansion which has occurred in the poultry industry and because of the large numbers which are often kept in relatively close confinement, disease has taken a greater toll of poultry than of any other form of livestock. Infectious diseases caused by filter-passing viruses

and other parasites, are of the greatest importance. The treatment of ailing birds—as a rule—is not an economic practice since during the time the treatment is being carried out these birds may continue to spread infection and be a potential danger to the rest of the flock. Furthermore, if they do recover by virtue of treatment such recovered birds usually remain as carriers and continue to spread infection for lengthy periods to susceptible stock and to contaminate the ground, housing and equipment. It has been rightly said that in poultry farming the health of the whole flock is of far more importance than the well-being of any of its individual units. Hygiene is of paramount importance in poultry husbandry and the best hospital is the incinerator.

306. There is an unfortunate belief that hygiene and sanitation are terms commonly connected with disease and usually only to be brought into force when disease has become apparent. Nothing is farther from the truth, the definition of hygiene is "the principles or science of health," and of sanitation "the removal of those conditions which may cause ill health." The two terms then are synonymous with good husbandry rather than disease.

307. It has been pointed out by economists that disease ranks second to food cost in egg production and may raise the price of one dozen eggs by as much as 8d. If the mortality is as high as 15 per cent, the profit per bird is three times that when mortality is 20 per cent and mortality of 25 per cent results in a trading loss. It has been pointed out that if the death rate is as high as two birds per 100 per month the balance sheet will show a loss.

308. Dirt and dust are the breeding place for all and the hiding place for many of the parasites and germs which affect poultry. These parasites will multiply most quickly in a warm, dark, humid atmosphere and poultry houses should be so constructed that no part can act as a permanent harbourer of dirt. For example, perches and nest boxes should be readily removable for regular cleansing and as has already been pointed out houses should be light and well ventilated. Walls, floors and ceilings should be free from those cracks and crevices which can harbour parasites, and they should be periodically cleaned down with a wash of hot lime and soft soap or sprayed with an emulsion of paraffin. These washes

can incorporate the new drugs such as DDT or Gammexane and which can usually be purchased ready made up under a variety of proprietary names.

309. Most of the bacterial diseases are transmitted by food and water which have been contaminated by infected excreta —obviously the food and water containers must be kept scrupulously clean and stale food should never be allowed to lie in the troughs to ferment. Aspergillosis for example is caused by a fungus found in musty food or litter. Clean water must be supplied at least daily—the vessels should not be "topped" but emptied, rinsed, and filled with fresh water.

310. Since many conditions, particularly parasitic diseases such as coccidiosis, are spread by infected droppings some form of regular cleaning is required. Essentially this means removal of the droppings and the parasites from possible contact with the host. The method by which this is done will depend on the form of management—wire floors, folds, droppings board, pits and so on. Some parasites such as the round worm are not infective to a new host until a period of up to ten days, but others such as the coccidial spore will, under the most optimum conditions for the parasite, reinfect in forty-eight hours. Cleaning of droppings boards and slattered floors and moving of folds should therefore be carried out every second day. Where bedding is used—as in some intensive laying houses, a thin layer which can be replaced frequently—say weekly—is preferable if the birds have access to range. Deep litter, used in completely intensively kept birds is a rather different story and based on the assumption that the fowls are free from parasites when housed. Incidentally, dirty litter and manure should not be composted near poultry runs since certain parasites can be wind-borne.

311. Some parasites require an intermediate host to complete their life history. The outstanding example in poultry is the tapeworm, the eggs of which are passed in the droppings but cannot infest a new host until they have matured inside certain species of slugs and snails. Prevention of these diseases depends on destruction of the intermediate hosts by dressing the pens with copper sulphate (1 lb. $CuSO_4$ in 50 gals. water per 100 square yards).

312. Fowls become predisposed to certain diseases, particularly the respiratory groups—colds, coryza, and fowl-pox—

by bad housing, faulty ventilators, overcrowding, dampness and draughts which cause the birds to crowd in corners. Nutritional deficiencies—in particular lack of vitamin A—lower the resistance to these diseases.

313. Again, depending on the type of management, birds pass during the course of their life from one type of housing to another. This should never take place until the new accommodation has been thoroughly cleaned. The following general lines should be adopted. First, after removal of the outgoing birds, spray the interior of the house and litter with an approved disinfectant in the strength recommended by the manufacturer. This lays the dust and helps to disinfect the bedding. Then scrape the walls, roof and floor and remove the scrapings and litter to the manure heap. If there is any question of disease having been present these scrapings should be burnt or buried. The interior of the house should then be scrubbed with 4 per cent washing soda in hot water—not only is this an excellent disinfectant—but it helps to dissolve the grease and dirt which inactivate disinfectants. Some poultrymen rely too much on disinfectants and it has been said that, "If cleaning is properly done there will be no germs left to disinfect and if cleaning is not thoroughly done most disinfectants will be inefficient." The importance of preliminary cleaning cannot be too strongly emphasized. Finally, doors and windows should be left open to help to dry out the house and to obtain the maximum exposure to sunlight before the new birds are installed. If disease has been present a second spraying of the house with a disinfectant is desirable. Utensils, brooms, scrapers, buckets, and so on must be similarly treated. In the case of coccidiosis the final spraying should be carried out with a 10 per cent solution of ammonia—the most effective lethal agent against the coccidial oocyst. The disinfection of second-hand utensils must be even more rigorous.

314. The disinfection of incubators and hatching premises for the control of egg-borne disease has been dealt with in the chapter on incubation. In general terms, however, it means employing a disinfectant which is lethal to microbes but which does not harm the developing embryo. So far, fumigation with formaldehyde gas has proved the most effective method.

315. Many parasites remain alive in the soil as well as in the houses—some for periods of more than a year. This must be borne in mind when arranging pen rotations. Pens that have been used should be ploughed, limed at the rate of two tons to the acre, re-seeded and left vacant for as long as possible. Where spare land is not available, advantage can be taken of the fact that the highest concentration of infected droppings is likely in the immediate vicinity of the house. The soil from this area alone can be removed, the exposed sub-soil sprayed with disinfectant, filled up with clinkers and a top layer of fresh soil put on. Alternatively, the house can be moved and the infected area fenced off. Grass in runs must always be kept short by grazing or mechanically, so that the droppings are exposed to the elements. Long grass which provides shade, moisture and warmth favours the survival of infective agents.

316. Adult birds often harbour parasites without exhibiting symptoms of ill-health but they are a potential danger to young stock. If possible therefore keep a separate rearing ground. Similarly, certain species of birds can infect other species—the fowl is seldom affected with blackhead but can infect turkeys—and different species of poultry should not be run together.

317. Special care must be taken with newly purchased stock or birds delivered from other premises, laying trials, and shows. They should always be isolated for twenty-one days and tested for both Bacillary White Diarrhoea and Tuberculosis before mixing with the home flock. Never purchase from dealers or markets but only from poultry farmers, the history of whose flock is known to you.

318. A live diseased fowl is the greatest source of infection and all ailing and unthrifty birds should be removed from the flock on the first evidence of ill-health. Certain diseases require special hygiene measures and it is essential therefore that in all cases of mortality an authoritative diagnosis should be made. Utilise the available laboratory and advisory service and do it quickly.

319. Good hygiene is also a question of economics. Unthrifty birds are unprofitable, and disease is one of the greatest threats to any livestock venture. Dirty eggs, apart from potentially spreading disease to incubators, fetch a lower

price and bad marketing will adversely affect the whole industry. Collect eggs frequently in clean containers. Supply an adequate number of nest boxes and keep the nest box litter clean. Never wipe or wash dirty eggs—this hastens the penetration of germs—they should be cleaned by scraping or with wire wool. Store eggs in a cool dry place.

320. Rats, apart from being the carriers of many diseases, can consume an amazing amount of food, kill chicks, injure older birds, and damage buildings. Mice also are a menace, and vermin control and the use of vermin-proof food stores are an important part of sanitation. Insect pests, flies, blue-bottles, etc. can also carry infection and they can be controlled by good management of manure heaps and the use of such substances as D.D.T. and gammexane.

321. One writer has admirably summarised the main points of good hygiene under the title of "A sanitary programme for the Poultry Farm."

(1) Avoid traffic in live birds
(2) Buy stock only from known sources
(3) Keep young stock away from older birds
(4) Dispose of dead birds properly by burning or burial
(5) Do not allow contaminated equipment to be brought on your premises
(6) Discourage visitors to poultry houses or runs
(7) Isolate all poultry returned from other premises
(8) Dispose of sick birds by slaughter
(9) Treat droppings as potential disease-spreaders
(10) Eliminate rats, mice and other pests
(11) Keep different species of birds segregated
(12) Do not sell birds known to be diseased or to have been in contact with disease
(13) Observe the strictest cleanliness in the houses, equipment and food stores
(14) Should disease appear, seek authoritative advice promptly

Recommended Books on Disease

Some Diseases of Poultry—Ministry of Agriculture Bulletin No. 6, published by H.M. Stationery Office.

Handbook on Poultry Diseases (Second Edition) issued by the National Veterinary Medical Association of Great Britain and Ireland (N.V.M.A. Publications No. 15).

INDEX